This annual belongs to...

Adyn Martin

PONY THE ANNUAL 2020

Inside your annual...

Published by DJ Murphy (Publishers) Ltd, Marlborough House, Headley Road, Grayshott, Surrey GU26 6LG

Who did what in PONY – The Annual
Contributors Jo Browne, Jessica Lewis, Rachel Dyke, Bethany Searby, Rebecca Philpot, Megan Hurley, Brigit Colclough
Design Adam Witt, Lizzi Porter, Jake Booth

PONY magazine is published every four weeks. To find out more about PONY magazine, visit ponymag.com
© Copyright DJ Murphy (Publishers) Ltd 2019

Printed by Graphicom via dell'Industria – 36100 Vicenza, Italy

ISBN 978-0-9928279-6-0

Look for the pages with this star and try our fab makes

12

16

82

88

Forever FRIENDS

Create a super-strong bond with your pony BFF

Sharing a close bond with your fave pony is soooo special and there's nothing like the feeling you'll get from knowing he loves you just as much as you adore him. It can even help your riding, too, because he'll trust you loads and he'll be happy to try anything for you. Here are seven great ways to build a super-strong bond...

1 CHILL OUT TOGETHER

Spending loads of quality time with your fave pony is really important if you want to build a bond with him, so don't just go to see him when you want to ride. Set aside 10-20 mins once or twice a week to give him a thorough groom and pamper sesh, which he'll love. Tie him up on the yard, or in his stable if it's light enough, and let him munch on a haynet while you spoil him.

2 SCRATCH HIS ITCHY SPOT

Most ponies love to be scratched and usually have a fave place where they like to get a bit of extra attention, such as their neck or withers. To work out what your pony likes best, start with gentle pressure and see how he responds. You'll know you've hit the right spot because he'll lean into you and may even pull a funny face!

TOP TIP
You can scratch your pony with your fingertips, or use a rubber curry comb in a circular motion.

DID YOU KNOW?
It's possible to form a close bond with a riding school pony. Find out if you can groom him after your lesson or book an own-a-pony day in the hols so you can spend extra time with him!

3 CARE FOR HIM

A pony will often form a bond with the person who looks after him – it makes sense as he'll associate you with nice things, such as serving up his dinner or turning him out in the field! So, try and get involved with your pony's care as much as you can, even if it's just at weekends.

4 KEEP TO A ROUTINE

Ponies thrive on having a routine, and your pony will feel safe and happy if he's fed, turned out and brought in from the field at around the same time each day. Meeting his needs in this way will help him put his trust in you.

5 REASSURE HIM

A great way to earn your pony's trust is to reassure him when he's worried about something. If you give him a pat or scratch and speak to him in a soothing voice, he'll realise everything's okay and he'll always feel confident when he's with you.

6 HELP HIM FEEL SAFE

Treat your fave pony like you'd want to be treated, so be considerate when handling him. Don't make sudden movements that could startle him, for example, and remove his bridle gently, so you don't bang his teeth with the bit. He'll enjoy being around you so much more.

TOP TIP
Don't think that food is the way to a pony's heart, because giving him lots of treats could make him bargy and nippy.

7 MAKE THINGS FUN

Doing the same thing all the time can be boring for your pony, but he'll love his work if you make it interesting for him. So, swap the school for a fun hack once or twice a week, and include some poles in your flatwork sessions to mix things up! You could also set up a handy pony-style course to tackle, or try groundwork for a change.

Gear guide

As well as your normal riding gear, a body protector is a must for cross-country. You should also wear a riding hat without a fixed peak, such as a skull cap. If you have an air jacket, you can pop it over the top of your body protector.

Some ponies get excited in open spaces, so you may need a different bit or noseband that gives you extra control – ask your instructor for advice and always try out any new kit in an arena first. Well-fitting boots are a good idea to protect your pony's legs, too.

FEEL LIKE
Flying

Cross-country is one of the most amazing things you can do with your fave pony

Going cross-country is super-exciting and few things compare to the feeling you'll get from cantering across open countryside and soaring over natural fences on your fave pony. If you'd like to have a go, here's all you need to know.

Be prepared
Just like with any other ridden activity, you'll need to make sure your pony's thoroughly warmed up before you start jumping. Begin in walk, encouraging him to march forward, then move up into trot and ride a few straight lines and shapes, such as circles. When you pop him into canter, start in a steady pace before asking him to open up and lengthen his stride for a few steps, then bring him back to working canter again.

Building confidence
You should always begin with an easy, inviting fence to get you and your pony off to a confident start. So, look for a small log, rolltop or pheasant feeder and approach it in a positive canter rhythm. Look up and over the fence and wrap your legs around your pony's sides to encourage him forward. Pop over it two or three times, then jump a couple more straightforward fences. If you have a young pony, this could be enough for his first cross-country outing, but if your pony's experienced and jumping confidently, you can think about trying some of the more challenging obstacles you'll find on a course.

Ditch it

Plain ditches don't involve any height, but lots of riders and ponies find them super-spooky! The secret to clearing them is to ride positively forward and keep your eyes up. If you look down into the ditch, your pony's much more likely to stop. Always start in walk when introducing a new ditch to your pony, then approach in trot and canter when you're both feeling confident.

Corner to corner

Corner fences are narrow at one end and wide at the other, and the secret to acing them is to aim your pony at exactly the right spot! If you try to jump the wide end he'll have to make a really big leap to clear it, and if you go for the narrow side he's more likely to run out. So, you need to aim for somewhere in the middle! It can help to imagine a straight line going from the middle of the wide end to the point of the narrow end – aiming for this line will help you keep a straight approach, rather than arriving at the jump on an angle.

Straight and narrow

Narrow fences are often called skinnies, and the challenge is to keep your pony super-straight or he could duck out to the side. It can help to stay in trot when you're first introducing them, so you have more control. Your riding position is super-important with this type of fence, so sit up tall with your shoulders back. Squeeze your pony with your legs and open your hands just a little to help guide him into the middle of the fence.

" Ride positively forward and keep your eyes up "

Water park

It's super-fun to splash through water – but first you've got to persuade your pony to get his feet wet! The best thing to do is ask a friend with an experienced pony to give you a lead. Follow them in at walk, wrapping your legs around your pony's sides to encourage him forward, but give him time to take a look and understand what you want him to do. If you try to hurry him in, it could make him more worried about getting wet.

When you're in the water, walk around to get him used to the feel of it splashing against his legs. Then try walking in and out by yourself, and gradually build up to trotting through the water.

DID YOU KNOW?
Cross-country fences have flags on either side – when jumping, keep the white flag on your left and the red one on the right.

Up and down

You'll often find steps on a course to ride up or down. There could be a single step to tackle or a set of two or three. When jumping up, squeeze your pony's sides with your legs to create enough energy to make the leap. Lean slightly forward and allow a little with your hands to give him the freedom to stretch out his neck. When jumping down, keep your shoulders back and your heels down to stop you tipping forward. Again, allow with your hands, but don't let your reins slip too much, to make sure you have control of your pony as soon as you land.

Want to have a go?

If you've been inspired to try cross-country, book a schooling sesh at a local course and ask your instructor to go with you. It's a good idea to ask a friend on an experienced pony to come, too, so they can give you a lead to start with. When you've been schooling a few times and your pony's familiar with different types of fence, why not enter a competition? You could have a go at a hunter trial class, or even a one-day event!

MAKE

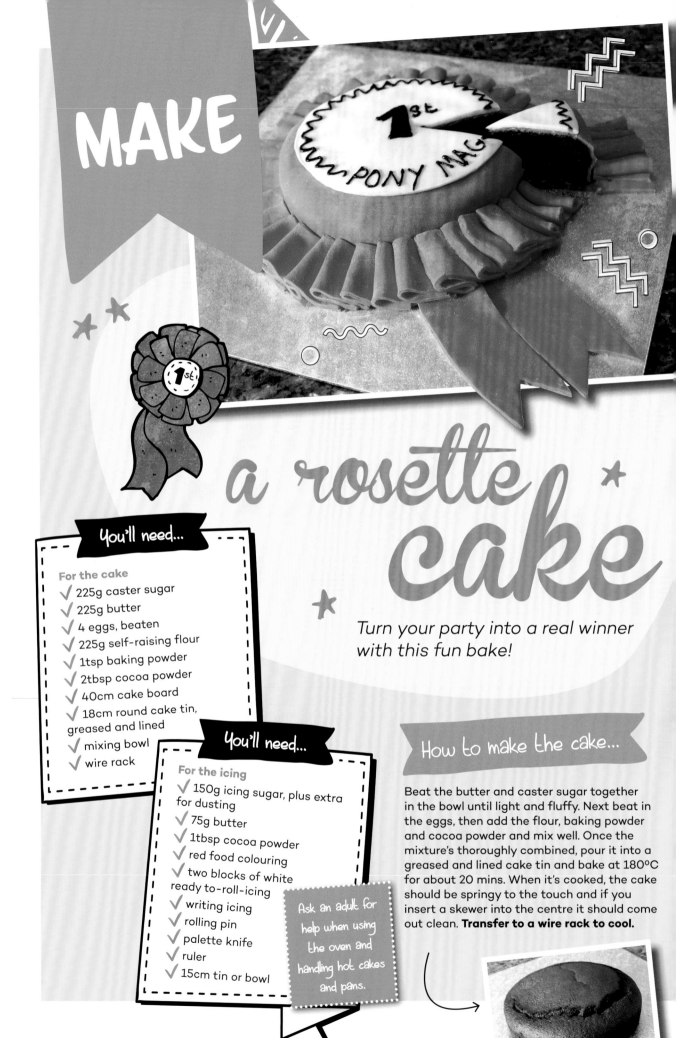

a rosette cake

Turn your party into a real winner with this fun bake!

You'll need...

For the cake
- ✓ 225g caster sugar
- ✓ 225g butter
- ✓ 4 eggs, beaten
- ✓ 225g self-raising flour
- ✓ 1tsp baking powder
- ✓ 2tbsp cocoa powder
- ✓ 40cm cake board
- ✓ 18cm round cake tin, greased and lined
- ✓ mixing bowl
- ✓ wire rack

You'll need...

For the icing
- ✓ 150g icing sugar, plus extra for dusting
- ✓ 75g butter
- ✓ 1tbsp cocoa powder
- ✓ red food colouring
- ✓ two blocks of white ready to-roll-icing
- ✓ writing icing
- ✓ rolling pin
- ✓ palette knife
- ✓ ruler
- ✓ 15cm tin or bowl

Ask an adult for help when using the oven and handling hot cakes and pans.

How to make the cake...

Beat the butter and caster sugar together in the bowl until light and fluffy. Next beat in the eggs, then add the flour, baking powder and cocoa powder and mix well. Once the mixture's thoroughly combined, pour it into a greased and lined cake tin and bake at 180°C for about 20 mins. When it's cooked, the cake should be springy to the touch and if you insert a skewer into the centre it should come out clean. **Transfer to a wire rack to cool.**

While the cake is cooling, you can prepare your icing.

1. Beat together the butter, cocoa powder and icing sugar to make butter cream. Leave in the fridge to chill until you're ready to use it.

2. Next, take one block of ready-to-roll-icing, add a few drops of red food colouring and knead it until the colour's evenly distributed. Keep adding a few drops at a time until your icing is the colour you'd like.

3. Position your cake in the centre of the board, using a small amount of buttercream to hold it in place. Now spread the rest of the buttercream evenly over the top and sides of the cake.

Ask an adult for help when using a knife.

4. Lightly dust a work surface and rolling pin with icing sugar, then roll out your coloured icing and drape it over the cake. Once it's completely covered, use your hands to gently push the icing onto the cake. Trim away any excess and put to one side.

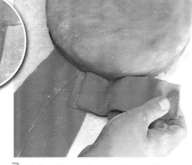

5. Combine the left-over coloured icing and roll it again. Cut it into strips that are 5cm wide and 15cm long.

6. Take two of the strips and cut a V into the ends, so it looks like a ribbon. Then place on the cake board to form the tail of your rosette.

7. Take the other strips of icing and place them all around the cake. Fold the icing back over itself, approx 2cm at a time, to make it look like pleated ribbon.

AWESOME!

8. To make the centre disc, roll out your white icing and carefully cut out a circle using a bowl or round tin as a guide. Add a few drops of water on the base of the disc, then carefully place it on top of your cake.

9. Finally add your decorations! Use writing icing to draw a 1st and make the cake into a winning red rosette!

TOP TIP
You can personalise your cake by adding a name!

IT'S pony time!

Make your life ponytastic!

We all love ponies, but if you're not lucky enough to have one of your own it can feel impossible to spend as much time with your fave animal as you'd like. But don't panic, here are a few ideas to help you get more ponies in your life.

Be a volunteer

There are tons of ways to get involved with ponies through volunteering! You can offer to help out at a RDA group or at a local show – they always need people to join the arena party. It's a great way to see loads of ponies and learn a lot, too.

Visit a charity

Equine charities hold loads of fun activities throughout the year. You'll often get to meet the equine residents and see what's involved with rescuing a pony. So, you can have fun and help ponies in need – perfect!

Live the dream

Have you always dreamed of exploring more of the gorgeous UK countryside on horseback? Riding centres across the country offer guided hacks and treks for all levels, so you could even get your parents involved, too.

If you're going on holiday abroad, why not find out if there are any cool places to ride near to where you're staying?

Groom for a friend

If you've got a friend with their own pony, why not offer to groom for them when they next go to a show? What could be better than spending a day with your friend, while surrounded by ponies?

Own a pony for a day

Most riding schools offer special days where you can see what it's like to look after a pony for the whole day! You'll get the chance to have riding lessons, as well as grooming your pony!

Spectate at a show

Look online to find out what exciting events are happening in your area. From eventing to county shows with showing and showjumping classes, there are plenty of opportunities to see some top equestrian action. Plus, if you're super-lucky you might even see your fave pro rider up close!

Go to camp

There's no better way to spend a week than at pony camp! You'll be responsible for taking care of a pony like he's your own, and have a whole week of lessons in all disciplines. Plus, you'll make amazing friends, create lifelong memories and might even be able to stay away for the week!

Go native

There are native ponies roaming free across some of the UK's national parks, so why not pay them a visit? Exmoor, Dartmoor and the New Forest have ponies galore. Connemara in Ireland offers the chance to spot some ponies, too.

Watch PONY videos

Why not visit the PONY YouTube channel? You'll find lots of pony care info and get to watch videos of super-cute ponies, too!

JUMP TO IT!

Check out why showjumping's the most amazing equestrian sport ever!

For many riders, showjumping is the ultimate test of the partnership they share with their horse or pony. You have to be totally in tune with each other to negotiate a course of coloured fences without any refusals or knock-downs. Trust is really important between you, too, so you can make split-second decisions in the jump-off that'll help you achieve a winning time.

DID YOU KNOW?
The world record for the highest fence jumped by a horse was set way back in 1949! Captain Alberto Larraguibel Morales of Chile and his horse, Huaso, cleared a huge 2.47m.

Get involved

One of the great things about showjumping is that anyone can have a go! Loads of shows start with cross-pole classes for nervous or beginner riders, or inexperienced ponies. You can even go to a show and just do the clear round class, which is a fun, no-pressure way to start your showjumping career!

If you're really bitten by the bug and want to compete more often and give yourself a challenge, many shows have a championship you can aim for. Or why not join British Showjumping and progress through the levels?

Ride in style

A big difference between showjumping and dressage and eventing is that you don't have your riding or your pony's paces scored. But this doesn't mean that flatwork isn't super-important. To increase your chances of clearing all the fences, you'll need to be an effective, accurate rider and your pony must be balanced, supple and stay in a rhythm. These can only be achieved through correct schooling.

For the high jump

A puissance is a showjumping class where the fences get higher and higher. It's held at shows like Olympia, where spectators love watching fearless riders and their horses take on the big red wall. The highest ever puissance wall jumped was an amazing 2.4m, which was cleared by German rider Franke Sloothaak riding Optiebeurs Golo in Belgium in 1991.

Puissance classes are sometimes included at local shows – would you be brave enough to have a go?

> **DID YOU KNOW?**
> The first ever showjumping class is believed to have taken place in Paris, France, in 1866.

> **DID YOU KNOW?**
> Scott Brash has also won the class that offers the most prize money – twice. He won the $1 million (£787,970) International Grand Prix at Spruce Meadows, Canada, in 2015 and 2016.

Derby day

One of the most famous showjumping competitions is the Hickstead Derby, which is held every summer. The riders have to negotiate a course of challenging obstacles, including persuading their horse to descend the super-steep, 10ft 6in high bank! Clear rounds are usually few and far between, but some riders have proved to be Derby specialists, including William Funnell who's won the class four times!

Winner, winner!

Like eventing, the sport of showjumping has a Grand Slam, and there's a €1 million (£890,000) bonus up for grabs for winning three major competitions in a row. So far, Scott Brash is the only rider to have achieved the triple, making history in 2015.

The Rolex Showjumping Grand Slam now includes a fourth show. If a rider wins this as well, they'll get another €1 million Euros – wow!

WHERE ONLY WILD HORSES WALK

When Indigo is separated from his herd, he needs to fight for survival. By Rebecca Loftus

I remember it as if it was yesterday. I was laying there, beside my mum. There was a full moon, and a light breeze gently swayed the trees. Mum jumped up, the whites of her eyes showing. "Wolf!" she cried. She pushed me with her nose. "Run, run or he'll catch you." I stumbled as I got to my feet, but finally found my balance.

I galloped and galloped as fast as my long foal legs could carry me. I ran out of the meadow and through the dense brush, and when I could run no more I stopped. I looked behind me, I was alone and far away from home. I didn't know how long it would be until I saw my mum again.

Face your fears

I walked on, hoping to see something or someone familiar. The sun started to peek up from the horizon and the golden sky reminded me of my mum. Her coat was that colour. Tears welled up in my eyes at the thought of her. Every night before I went to sleep, she'd say "Indigo, never be afraid to face your fears." Now I'm facing the fear of being all alone.

I came to a mountain on my journey – it was wide and tall, and I couldn't see any way round it. I looked up at the mountain. "Never be afraid to face your fears," I repeated to myself.

The first part of the climb was tricky as it was so steep. I stumbled and grazed my forelegs, but I kept going. After an hour or so I finally reached the top. It was an amazing view. A vast plain of grass stretched into the distance with a creek running through it.

My stomach rumbled loudly. I was hungry and my mouth was as dry as dust. I spotted a trail that led downward, and didn't think twice. I cantered towards it and slid down. At the bottom I tumbled, legs going in all directions, but I didn't care. I picked myself up and munched on the oh so sweet grass.

After a few mouthfuls I headed for the creek and splashed into it. The cool water soothed my cuts and bruises and I took a long drink, which felt so good. My dry mouth softened at that first gulp of water.

My herd had spoken of a healing creek, in the direction of the setting sun, although I hadn't believed it. I felt safe here, but as I splashed and drenched myself I realised I had to continue my journey. I took a look at my reflection in the water. I could no longer see my ribs and my cuts had disappeared. I looked up, just as the sun was setting.

Lightning bolt

I knew my luck would eventually run out, and I was right. A week or so later I was walking through a forest when I noticed a strange smell. I sniffed the air. "Storm," I whispered. Just then, lightning struck a tree nearby. I heard a creaking and cracking as a large fir tree crashed just behind me. I galloped off in fright. I'd experienced storms before, when I was with my herd, but never as bad as this. Not taking heed of where I was going, I stumbled over some broken roots. As I fell, I hit my head on a rock. Blackness.

A fight for life

I was lying beside my mother. There was a full moon and a light summer breeze gently swayed the trees. Then my dream was interrupted by a blood-curdling howl.

I woke up, startled, and heard another howl. I got to my feet and looked around warily. Then I saw them. Ten wolves with bared teeth, all snarling. I reared up. One wolf jumped on my back, digging his claws into me. I cried out in pain, and began to buck madly. I threw him off and he fell against a tree. A few of the wolves backed off, obviously scared, but another lunged at me, teeth bared. I reared up and brought my hooves down on his shoulder. He yelped, and limped off.

Now it was just me and the alpha male. His hackles were raised and his yellow teeth bared. I raised my hoof and tossed my head up and down, ready to attack. He ran at me, growling angrily. I was about to run forward, but hesitated. I remembered a trick my mother taught me. "Wait for the enemy to come," she'd said. "Then jump and turn on your side."

I waited for the wolf to come. A fraction of a second before he sunk his teeth into me, I jumped. In mid-air I turned onto my side and came falling down. The wolf lay there, winded for a moment, then slunk back into the trees along with the rest of his pack. I got up and shook myself off. I wasn't afraid any more.

A change in the air

I was exhausted after the fight with the wolves, and must have slept for at least a day. When I woke up, the sun was shining down on me. I stood up gingerly, because I was sore from where I'd been scratched and bitten by the wolves, and from falling on my side. But maybe it was a small price to pay, I thought to myself – pain in return for still being alive.

I stiffly trotted out of the woods and into a field of pale blue daisies. It was magnificent. Just then, a strange animal streaked out in front of me. He had long ears, a fluffy round tail and a twitchy nose. As quickly as he arrived, the twitchy-nosed-fluffy-tailed-long-eared thing sprinted off, so I followed him. I must have chased him for ages, and when I looked up there was another mountain.

> **Ten wolves with bared teeth were all snarling at me**

Safe again

I climbed the mountain and below I could see a herd of horses. I didn't recognise them at first, but then I saw a mare with a distinctive golden coat. It was my herd!

I burst into a canter, and raced down to them, through the bush and into the meadow. "Mum," I cried. "Mum!" The mare turned her head. "Indigo! Indigo, my love," she called as she cantered towards me. We slowed down and came to a halt and our necks intertwined in a loving hug. Mum stood back and took a long look at me. Her eyes began to well up with tears. "Oh, Indigo, look how much you have grown," she said. "I've missed you so much."

I wandered over to a nearby creek and looked down at my reflection. I barely recognised the horse that was looking back at me. My scruffy foal fluff had gone and in its place my coat was a lovely blue roan colour. I laughed. "I think everything will be okay now," I said.

That was six years ago. I led my herd to the field with the healing creek, and we've lived there happily ever since. I have my own foal now, too, a pinto filly called Meadow.

If I learned anything from my journey it was to face my fear, as Mum had always urged me to. You may not like doing it, but you certainly won't be afraid any more.

QUIZ

GUESS WHO?

Are you a celeb rider guru? Test your knowledge of top riders with this mega quiz

1. **Olympic eventer Mark Todd is originally from...**

   A Australia

   B USA

   C New Zealand

2. **What was Charlotte Dujardin and Valegro's score when they won individual gold in dressage at the 2012 London Olympics?**

   A 80.089%

   B 85.089%

   C 90.089%

3. **Which legendary eventer has won Badminton Horse Trials more times than any other rider?**

   A William Fox-Pitt

   B Lucinda Green

   C Mark Todd

4. **Emily King is the daughter of which famous eventer?**

   A Kitty King

   B Mary King

   C Lizzie King

5. **How many Olympic Games has dressage superstar Carl Hester competed at?**

   A 3

   B 2

   C 5

6. **John, Michael, Robert and William are all members of which famous showjumping family?**

   Ⓐ Wallace

   Ⓑ Whittard

   Ⓒ Whitaker

7. **In 2015, superstar German eventer Michael Jung won Burghley on his star horse La Biosthetique Sam, but why was the achievement so incredible?**

   Ⓐ He was riding with a broken ankle

   Ⓑ His reins broke half-way round

   Ⓒ His stirrup came off at the water jump

8. **Paralympian Sophie Wells has an allergy to...**

   Ⓐ Bananas

   Ⓑ Hay

   Ⓒ Horses

9. **Which top rider wrote the Tilly's Pony Tales series of books?**

   Ⓐ Alice Oppenheimer

   Ⓑ Pippa Funnell

   Ⓒ Jess Mendoza

10. **What is 2019 Badminton Horse Trials winner Piggy French's real first name?**

    Ⓐ Georgina

    Ⓑ Philippa

    Ⓒ Rosie

11. **Eventer Ben Hobday completed Badminton three times on...**

    Ⓐ Mulrys Mistake

    Ⓑ Mulrys Error

    Ⓒ Mulrys Muddle

12. **What is the name of Nick Skelton's gold medal winning showjumper at Rio 2018?**

    Ⓐ Supernova II

    Ⓑ Big Star

    Ⓒ Harvest Moon

Turn to page 100 to find out how you got on!

TOKYO 2020

Olympic and Paralympic Games

Find out all you need to know about Tokyo 2020

DID YOU KNOW?
Host country Japan has only ever won one Olympic equestrian medal. Takeichi Nishi and Uranus won showjumping gold in 1932.

It's a super-exciting year for equestrian sport with the Tokyo 2020 Olympic and Paralympic Games taking place in the summer, when you'll be able to cheer on your fave riders and horses from around the world. Here are some super-cool facts about these amazing events, including why the format for the equestrian disciplines is going to be different this time round.

The timetable

Tokyo 2020 runs from 24 July – 9 August, and the Paralympic Games from 25 August – 6 September

Here's when the equestrian competitions will take place...
- **dressage** 25-26 and 28-29 July
- **eventing** 31 July – 3 August
- **showjumping** 4-5 and 7-8 August
- **para-dressage** 27-31 August

JAPAN

Something old, something new

Most of the equestrian action will take place in Tokyo's Equestrian Park, which was actually used when the city hosted the Olympics in 1964! Event riders and spectators will get to experience something extra special on cross-country day, as a temporary course is being constructed on a piece of reclaimed land in Tokyo Bay! It'll offer horses, riders and competitors an amazing view of the city in the background.

Team talk

At Tokyo 2020, equestrian teams will be made up of three horses and riders, not the usual four. The reason behind the change is that it'll allow more countries the chance to take part, and make things more exciting for spectators. However, it means every team member's performance counts and the worst score can't be discarded.

Teams may take a reserve horse and rider, who can be drafted in for a medical or veterinary reason. In eventing, there's a proposed format to allow teams to complete if things don't go to plan for any of their riders, but they'll pick up costly penalties.

TOKYO 2020
FAST FACTS

DRESSAGE

● everyone rides a Grand Prix test that's a qualifier for individual and team medals
● riders will compete in groups, with the 18 highest scorers going into the Freestyle, where they'll dance to music to try and win an individual medal
● the top eight teams qualify for the Grand Prix Special test, which will decide who wins the team medals

SHOWJUMPING

● individual awards will now be decided before team medals
● the 30 highest placed riders in round one qualify for the individual final
● only the top 10 teams will jump for a medal

EVENTING

● the dressage test will be shorter than usual
● there will be two showjumping rounds – one to decide team medals and one for individual placings

PARA-DRESSAGE

● there'll be three competitions – individual, team and freestyle to music
● individual and freestyle tests are divided into five grades, so riders compete on equal terms
● only the highest eight riders in each grade will qualify for the freestyle to music

READ MY MIND

Solve common pony problems by working out what he's thinking

It can be really frustrating if your fave pony behaves a certain way or doesn't do what you want him to. But it's important to remember that ponies aren't naughty on purpose, and there's sure to be a really good reason why he's acting this way. Taking a look at things from his point of view will help you understand his behaviour, so you can find the best way to solve any problems you're having.

TOP TIP
If you're worried about your pony's behaviour, get some expert help. Speak to your instructor, your yard manager or a qualified equine behaviourist.

FEELING SPOOKY

What's happening Even just a glimpse of a dustbin, plastic bag or traffic cone has your pony leaping sideways, running backwards or turning for home.

What he's thinking "That scary thing over there might eat me!"

Change how he feels

Show him these objects aren't anything to worry about by spook-proofing him in the arena. Set out some things that you might see when hacking, then gradually work him closer to them. Reassuring him with your voice will help him feel safe and build his confidence.

DID YOU KNOW?
In the wild, ponies are prey animals, and they have to be super-careful or they might end up as someone's lunch! This means they're always on the lookout for potential danger.

CAN'T CATCH ME!

What's happening When you go to bring your pony in for a ride, he trots off to the furthest corner of the field. Not so great when you're meeting your friend in 15 mins!

What he's thinking "You're only interested in spending time with me when you want to go for a ride. That seems too much like hard work, and I'd much rather stay in my field munching grass."

Change how he feels

Make sure you bring him in for fun things, not just for work. So, instead of schooling him, treat him to a relaxing grooming session or bring him onto the yard for a small feed, then turn him out again. He'll soon be really pleased to see you!

A LOAD ON YOUR MIND

What's happening Your pony refuses to walk up the ramp into the trailer or lorry.

What he's thinking "You really think I'm going into that small, dark, enclosed space? No way!"

DID YOU KNOW?
Ponies are naturally claustrophobic, which can make them wary of enclosed spaces.

Change how he feels

Regularly practise loading your pony, so that when you want to go to a show or lesson he'll follow you straight in. It's important you always take your time and don't rush him, or he'll really think loading's something to worry about. Also, make the space as inviting as possible for him by hanging up a tasty haynet, and lower the front ramp if you're using a trailer to let lots of light in.

TOP TIP
Regularly feeding your pony in the lorry or trailer will help him associate loading with nice things.

LEAD THE WAY

What's happening Your fave pony pulls or pushes you around when you lead him.

What he's thinking "Hey, there's grass over there – I'm off to get some!"

Change how he feels

You spend more time with your fave pony on the ground than riding him, so it's super-important he's polite to lead and handle. Practising groundwork is a great way to help with this. Start with simple halt-walk-halt transitions, then try leading him around obstacles. Weave in and out of cones, or make an S-bend out of jumping poles that you can walk him through.

TOP TIP
Leading your pony in his bridle can give you extra control.

HIDE AND SEEK

Ponies like to play, too!

Gem as **Biscuit**

Lily as **Coco**

Ruby as **Amelia**

HAFLINGER

From humble beginnings to earning royal favour, there's far more to these golden beauties than meets the eye

With their shiny golden coat and flowing mane and tail, Haflingers are easily recognisable. Originally from Austria, these mountain horses prove it's possible to be tough and beautiful.

History

All Haflingers are descended from a stallion called Folie 249, who was born in 1874. His mother was a Tyrolean mountain horse and his father a half-Arab stallion. Haflingers were originally used as workhorses by people living in the Austrian Alps, including as a packhorse and for forestry. As the mountain farmers could usually only afford to keep one horse, Haflingers had to be able to do all the work and be handled by the whole family, including children and elderly people.

During World War I and II, Haflingers were in huge demand as pack horses because they were strong, tough and willing to work in difficult conditions. They even went as far as Russia due to their ability to survive cold temperatures.

DID YOU KNOW?
Haflinger stallions come from one of seven bloodlines – A, B, M, N, S, ST and W. You can tell which bloodline a stallion comes from because his name will start with that letter.

DID YOU KNOW?
Even though they're often smaller than 14.2hh, Haflingers are called horses, not ponies.

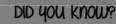

FACT FILE

HEIGHT: 13.3hh-14.3hh, although particularly good examples of the breed are allowed to be taller.
COLOUR: Chestnut with a flaxen mane and tail, in all shades from pale gold to dark liver chestnut and usually with a lighter belly and legs. White face markings, such as blazes and stars, are common.
PLACE OF ORIGIN: The Tyrol region of Austria.
KNOWN FOR: Their intelligence, big personality, work ethic and kind temperament.

Home of the Haflinger

The Haflinger Breeders' Association of Tyrol is based at the Fohlenhof in Ebbs, Austria. In Tyrol, it's not permitted to privately own a Haflinger stallion – they're all owned by the state – and every year, the 25 best colts born in Tyrol are selected to live at the Fohlenhof. During the winter, the colts stay in large, indoor paddocks and enjoy up to five hours of turnout every day in groups, even when it's snowing. In May, they're walked up to mountain pastures – known as alms – where they roam free for the summer and autumn. When they're three years old, they're inspected again before standing at stud, both at the Fohlenhof and all over the world.

DID YOU KNOW?
Mares and foals will also spend summers in the alms, but are usually brought back down in September before it gets too cold.

DID YOU KNOW?
The passport of a registered Haflinger includes seven generations to show his pure breeding.

By royal appointment

In 1969, Queen Elizabeth II visited Austria and was given two Haflinger mares as a gift. The mares were brought back to the UK, and the Queen has bred Haflingers ever since. She keeps them at Balmoral in Scotland, where they work on the castle's estate, and they're often seen in showing classes at Royal Windsor Horse Show. Prince Philip competed in driving classes with a team of Haflingers, too.

The Haflinger today

The versatility that made the original Haflingers so useful to Tyrolean farmers means they're able to turn their hooves to just about anything. This includes trekking, dressage, jumping, driving, vaulting, endurance and showing, and their generous nature makes them popular as children's ponies, too. From one tiny corner of Austria, these beautiful horses have travelled all over the world, going as far as India, Namibia, Brazil and Australia!

IT'S A *pole* LOTTA FUN

J ust riding shapes in the arena can get a bit boring, so why not change things up with some polework? Not only is it waaay more fun, it's great for your pony, too! Riding over poles can help improve his core strength, straightness, balance and rhythm, plus he'll need to watch where he's placing his feet, which will help him stay focused.

Jazz up your next schooling sesh with these fab polework exercises

TOP TIP
Ride each exercise the same number of times on both reins, to make sure your pony uses all of his muscles evenly.

TOP TIP
Set out the poles before you ride, so you don't have to keep getting off your pony during your session to move them around.

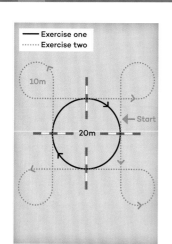

Exercise one ——
Exercise two ·······

10m

20m

← Start

THE CLOCK

There are two ways you can ride through this pole layout and it'll help you work on your pony's balance, bend and suppleness.

Set up
You'll need four poles set out on a 20m circle. Imagine you're creating a clock face with poles at 12, 3, 6 and 9 o'clock.

Round and round

Get warmed up

THE MAZE

This layout can create a fun warm-up for your pony, and allows you to ride a more challenging exercise, too!

Set up

Set out six poles in two interlocking C shapes, with one trot stride (1-1.3m) between the four central poles.

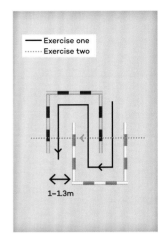

— Exercise one
······ Exercise two

1–1.3m

Poled over

Exercise one

Tick-tock clock

Use the poles to help you ride a perfect circle.

How to ride it

Starting in walk, circle over the poles, aiming for the centre of each one. Look around the circle and open your inside rein slightly to encourage your pony to bend, and keep your inside leg on the girth. When you're confident, try it in trot. If you find it difficult, ride a larger circle over the outside edge of the poles, before attempting a smaller one.

Exercise two

Round and round

Test your accuracy and balance.

How to ride it

Starting on the right rein, step over the first pole, then ride a 10m circle left. As you come out of the circle, go straight over your second pole then circle to the left again, so you're riding a 10m circle between each pair of poles. Try it on the other rein, this time circling to the right. If you'd like to up the challenge, have a go in trot.

Exercise one

Get warmed up

The ideal way to get your pony feeling supple.

How to ride it

Walk between the poles, so your pony bends through the S shape. Make sure you sit up tall and look in the direction you want your pony to go, and squeeze him with your legs to encourage him to march forward.

Exercise two

Poled over

Trotting poles can help improve your pony's impulsion and put a spring in his step!

How to ride it

Once you've weaved through the S shape, use the layout as trotting poles. In trot, approach from the end. Wrap your legs around your pony's sides to maintain his impulsion. Once you've ridden over the poles one way, change the rein and approach from the opposite direction.

TURN OVER FOR MORE FUN EXERCISES

THE KITE

Ace straight lines, circles and improve your accuracy with this fab layout.

Set up

Use four poles to form a diamond shape, then place a fifth pole across the centre.

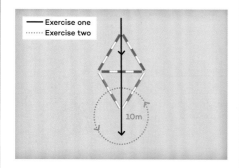

— Exercise one
···· Exercise two

10m

Point to point

Exercise one
Point to point

The points of this shape give you a guide for riding super-straight lines.

How to ride it

Walk straight through the kite, so you're going from one point to another. Make sure you have an even contact on both reins and wrap your legs around your pony's sides to help him stay straight. Next try riding the exercise in trot.

Exercise two
Cool circles

Riding over poles on a circle will help improve your pony's balance.

How to ride it

Ask your pony for a forward trot, then ride a 10m circle that goes through the left side of the kite. Aim to ride one or two strides of trot over the kite, making sure you maintain a regular rhythm. Then, change the rein and have a go the other way.

A new angle

Terrific transitions

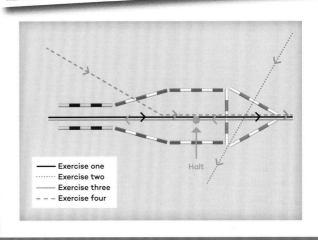

— Exercise one
······· Exercise two
— Exercise three
– – – Exercise four

Halt

THE ROCKET

This super-versatile layout lets you ace accurate lines, perfect transitions, and loads more!

Set up
Use your poles to create a rocket shape as shown in the diagram above. Build your rocket in the centre of the arena, to give you enough room to ride the exercises.

Exercise one
Super centre lines
Work on keeping your pony straight and acing centre lines.

How to ride it
In trot, approach the tail of the rocket and ride through the channel. Keep as straight as possible, aiming for the centre of the middle pole and riding out over the rocket's nose.

Exercise two
Stay straight
Another way to practise being super-straight and accurate.

How to ride it
In walk or trot, approach the nose of the rocket on a diagonal line. Enter over the middle of one pole, then exit over the opposite corner. Aiming for the corner will help you ride a straight line. Try this exercise from both directions.

Exercise three
Terrific transitions
Make sure your pony's really listening to you and test his straightness, too.

How to ride it
Ride straight through the nose of the rocket, making sure you're looking up and ahead to help your pony keep straight. When you reach the square in the middle, sit up tall and ask for a downward transition to halt. Count to three, then ask your pony to walk on again, staying straight to exit through the tail. If you'd like to make the exercise a little trickier, why not try a trot-halt-trot transition?

Exercise four
A new angle
Perfect for helping your fave pony's balance and core strength.

How to ride it
On the right rein, approach the angled side pole. As you ride over the pole, look left and turn towards the nose of the rocket. Help your pony make a smooth turn by placing your left leg on the girth and your right leg slightly behind it to encourage him to bend. Continue to ride straight, making sure your pony steps over the point of the triangle. Ride through on both reins, then try again in trot.

TO THE RESCUE

Alice couldn't be more in sync with her fave pony, Michael. But would their bond be able to save him when disaster struck?

I knew Michael was the perfect pony for me from the minute I saw him. I was at the New Forest pony sales with my dad. We'd just gone for a look – New Forests were my absolute fave breed and I'd been pestering my parents for ages to take me to see some in real life.

I'd never seen so many New Forests in one place before! All beautiful shades of chestnut and bay, they were patiently waiting to be shown off to potential buyers who were looking for their new best friend.

That's when I saw him.

He was a tiny pony, barely a year old, being gently encouraged into the sale ring by a group of men. I could see he needed someone to tell him everything would be alright. I knew that person was me.

I didn't even think. I quickly slipped away from Dad and coaxed the worried pony into the ring. "It's alright," I told him softly. "Someone really wonderful's going to take you home." He pricked his ears and followed me into the little arena.

Everyone was laughing that such a small girl had managed to do what the men hadn't, and I trotted with him round the ring to show him off to all the delighted people.

"SOLD!" cried the auctioneer, banging his gavel. I looked up and couldn't believe my eyes. Dad had just bought the pony – who I swiftly named Michael.

Just any other day

I've had Michael for five years now and it's been such fun growing up together. We love going out for hacks every weekend with my mum running alongside us – which is exactly what we'd planned to do the day disaster struck.

It was a bright Saturday morning. I'd eaten breakfast and Dad was getting ready to take my sister, Erin, to football practice. I put my plate in the dishwasher and asked Mum: "The usual route today?"

"Sounds good to me," she replied. "Why don't you get Michael ready, sweetheart, while I clear away and pop my trainers on."

> **I saw a gap in the fence and it hit me like a ton of bricks. My pony had escaped!**

I could hardly wait to get out of the door and run across the garden to Michael's field. I'm super-lucky to have enough room to keep Michael at home – I can even see him from my bedroom window!

Something's wrong

I rushed up to the field gate calling "Michael!" But I couldn't see my pony. Normally he canters over as soon as he hears my footsteps...

I tried again. "MICHAEL!" I yelled at the top of my voice, but he still didn't appear. Then I saw a gap in the fence and it hit me like a ton of bricks. My pony had escaped! I ran back to the house, trying to stay calm.

"Mum!" I shouted as soon as I reached the back door, "Michael's not in his field." Mum ran down the stairs. "Are you sure?" she replied. "Yes," I nodded frantically. "There's a hole in the fence, and I think he's got out."

"Right," said Mum, calmly. "He's bound to be somewhere on the farm. Go and get his headcollar and a bucket of feed and let's find him."

Finding Michael

After Mum rang the farmer next door, we headed through the gap in the fence and called for Michael again. We couldn't find him in the yard or any of the outbuildings. The only place left to check was the farmhouse garden.

It was a big, beautiful space that would've been a dream to explore when I was little. There was a small wooded area with crackly paths, a vast lawn for games and lots of beautiful flowers. I started to cry.

"Michael, where are you?" I called softly. As if in reply, I heard a whinny from the bottom of the garden – followed by a splash.

Confused, but relieved, Mum and I ran to find Michael. When I saw him I couldn't believe my eyes.

How did you get in there?

I stared down at Michael with my mouth open. He was in a swimming pool!

I ran to the edge, close to where he was standing looking terrified. "Oh Michael, what've you done!" I reached out and stroked his mane, which seemed to calm him down.

"He doesn't look hurt," Mum said, "but there's no way we're going to get him out without help." Meanwhile, the farmer had arrived and was just as shocked as we were. He said he'd love to help, but he wasn't quite sure how to do it safely. There was only one thing for it, we'd have to call the fire brigade.

Action stations

The fire brigade and our vet arrived in record time. Their plan was to sedate Michael to help him stay calm, then use a winch to lift him out of the pool. This meant they needed to get two straps under his belly to support him.

Once he was sedated, three of the firefighters jumped in to help Michael, but even with the medicine keeping him calm I could see he was scared. Here were three people he didn't know, splashing around while trying to pass something under his belly.

"Stop!" I cried, "Let me do it. He knows me, he trusts me. He'll just get more upset if you keep trying." Mum hesitated. "Are you sure you'll be safe, Alice?" she asked, giving me a worried look.

I smiled tightly at her. "I will be if you come with me and help keep him calm." She sighed. "Alright then, love, but let's both be careful." Mum and I got quietly into the pool. Michael's ears pricked forward as we neared him, but he was still breathing heavily.

"It's alright," I said soothingly, "we're just trying to help you. Good boy, we'll be done in a jiffy." Michael relaxed with the sound of my voice. Mum slipped a headcollar over his head and stood with him and we showed him the straps that we'd slip under his belly.

"They're nothing to be scared of," I told him, "it's no worse than the girth on your saddle." The straps needed to attach to a winch, which was poised above Michael. I just needed to pass them under his belly and hand them to a firefighter, who would attach it on the other side.

"Here goes," I thought. I held my breath and ducked under the water, holding the end of the first strap out as far under his belly as I could without getting too close. I felt the firefighter take it from me and I resurfaced carefully.

Michael was a bit startled when I re-emerged and he spooked – thankfully the strap had already been clipped into place. But now I was nervous. Would our bond be strong enough for Michael to trust me a second time?

I patted him gently. "We can do this, boy." I felt him relax again. I ducked beneath the surface one last time, passing the strap under. This time, Michael understood what we were doing and was as quiet as anything. The winch lifted him carefully out of the pool and, 30 seconds later, he was on dry land!

I felt so relieved, and hugged him harder than I've ever hugged him before.

All's well

Erin and Dad couldn't believe what had happened when they got back from football. Mum mended the fence while Michael spent the afternoon in the stable, munching on hay and warming up.

He was carefully checked over by the vet and was, thankfully, given the all clear after his ordeal. Thanks to our close friendship, we got through it together, and now our bond is stronger than ever!

MAKE pony treats & storage pot

Rustle up some super-tasty treats for your fave pony, and a cute jar to keep them in, too!

How to make the treat pot...

You'll need...

✓ a plastic jar (we used a 700g jar)
✓ sandpaper
✓ small model pony
✓ strong glue
✓ newspaper
✓ gold spray paint
✓ gloves
✓ dust mask

l. Wash the jar and lid, so there's no food left inside, and remove any sticky labels from the outside.

2. Lightly sand the hooves of your model pony and the top of the jar lid, to make the surfaces rough. Then ask an adult to help you glue the pony's hooves to the lid.

Always wear gloves and a dust mask when handling spray paint and ask an adult for help.

3. When the glue's dry, take the lid outside, put it on a piece of newspaper, then carefully spray it with gold paint.

4. Leave the lid in a sheltered, outside space to dry while you create your treats!

How to make apple flapjack treats...

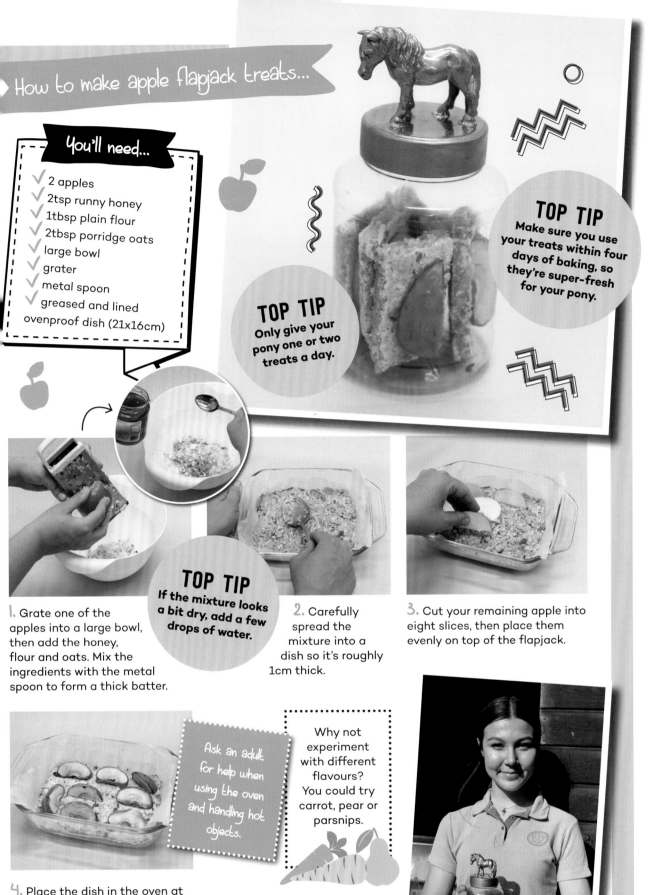

You'll need...

- ✓ 2 apples
- ✓ 2tsp runny honey
- ✓ 1tbsp plain flour
- ✓ 2tbsp porridge oats
- ✓ large bowl
- ✓ grater
- ✓ metal spoon
- ✓ greased and lined ovenproof dish (21x16cm)

TOP TIP
Only give your pony one or two treats a day.

TOP TIP
Make sure you use your treats within four days of baking, so they're super-fresh for your pony.

TOP TIP
If the mixture looks a bit dry, add a few drops of water.

1. Grate one of the apples into a large bowl, then add the honey, flour and oats. Mix the ingredients with the metal spoon to form a thick batter.

2. Carefully spread the mixture into a dish so it's roughly 1cm thick.

3. Cut your remaining apple into eight slices, then place them evenly on top of the flapjack.

Ask an adult for help when using the oven and handling hot objects.

Why not experiment with different flavours? You could try carrot, pear or parsnips.

4. Place the dish in the oven at 180°C for about 20 mins, or until the flapjack is golden brown. Using oven gloves, remove the treats from the oven.

5. When the flapjack has cooled, carefully cut it into eight bars. Put them in your treat pot and take to the yard!

TA-DAH!

24 HOURS

in the life of a pony

Ever wondered what a pony gets up to all day and all night? Check out Rocky's diary to find out

7.15am

I'm woken up by my fave sound – rattling buckets – as Karen, the yard manager, brings everyone's breakfast round. I only get a handful of chaff, but it's a tasty way to start the day. I like to tip my bucket upside down to make sure I haven't missed any!

7.45am

My owner, Jess, calls in on her way to school. She's always in a rush in the morning, but makes time to give me a hug before she leads me out to my paddock. It's going to be a fine spring day, so I won't need a rug on, but Jess sprays me with fly repellent in case there are any annoying bugs around.

8am

I share a paddock with my best pony pal, Freddie, but we don't waste time catching up first thing. We put our heads down and start munching straightaway!

Mornings are for munching!

10am

When we're feeling full we stop eating and rest up. I have a quick snooze in the sun while Freddie watches over me, then we swap over – there's usually nothing dangerous around, but it's always worth keeping an eye out!

12 noon

When I've finished dozing I feel thirsty, so I have a long, refreshing drink of water. Then Freddie and I nibble on a bit more grass.

2pm

My coat's a bit itchy, so I get down to roll. There's a spot I can't reach, so I persuade Freddie to scratch just behind my withers with his teeth, and I return the favour.

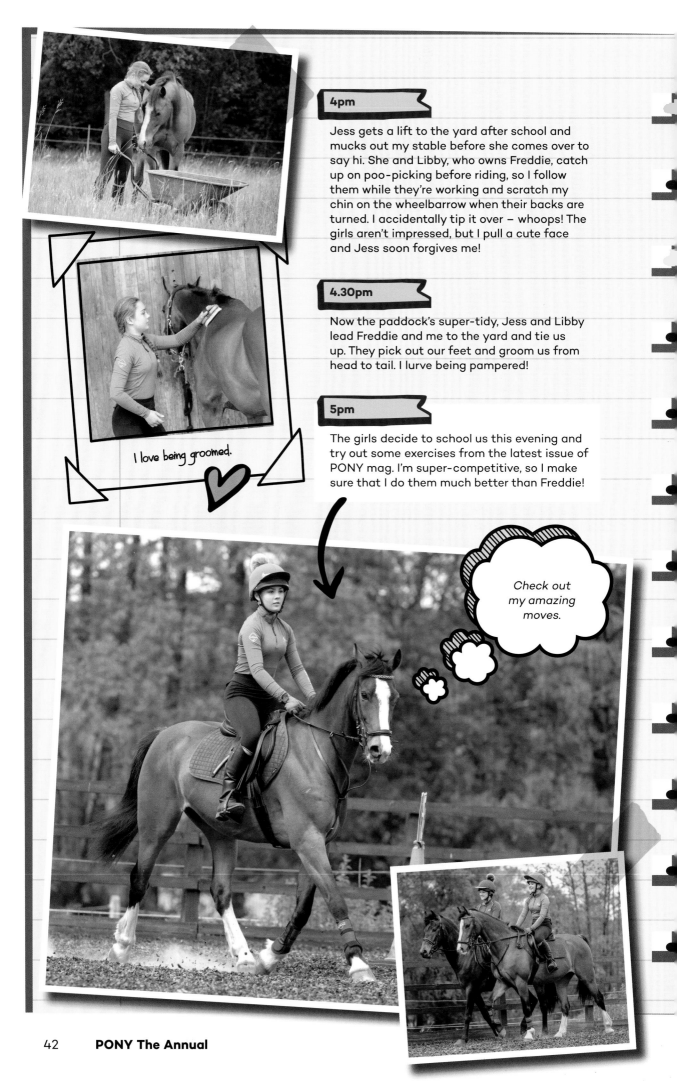

4pm

Jess gets a lift to the yard after school and mucks out my stable before she comes over to say hi. She and Libby, who owns Freddie, catch up on poo-picking before riding, so I follow them while they're working and scratch my chin on the wheelbarrow when their backs are turned. I accidentally tip it over – whoops! The girls aren't impressed, but I pull a cute face and Jess soon forgives me!

4.30pm

Now the paddock's super-tidy, Jess and Libby lead Freddie and me to the yard and tie us up. They pick out our feet and groom us from head to tail. I lurve being pampered!

5pm

The girls decide to school us this evening and try out some exercises from the latest issue of PONY mag. I'm super-competitive, so I make sure that I do them much better than Freddie!

I love being groomed.

Check out my amazing moves.

Night time

6.30pm

After we've cooled down from our schooling session, the girls lead us back to the yard where they untack and sponge off any sweat. Then Jess pops me into my stable – I have a feed balancer to nibble on, which gives me all my vits and mins – and a small haynet to keep me occupied.

BEST DAY

7pm

I pop my head over the stable door to neigh goodbye to Jess as her mum's arrived to take her home.

9.30pm

Karen comes round to say goodnight and top up our hay. I get two more small haynets, but annoyingly she ties them at either end of the stable – she says the exercise is good for me!

11.30pm

Ponies only need to sleep for a few hours a day, and while I sometimes snooze standing up, I need to lie down to get some proper rest. So, I snuggle into my soft shavings bed, drift off and I'm soon dreaming about my fave thing – food!

3am

I'm feeling refreshed after my sleep, and a little peckish, so I investigate my haynets to see what's left. Mid-munch I peek over my stable door to see what everyone's up to – I spot the yard cat looking for mice, but everything else is quiet. I whinny a quick hello to Freddie, who neighs back.

4am

My hay's nearly all gone, so I have a drink, then doze on and off until breakfast time.

WHY WE LOVE PONIES

We can all agree that ponies are the most amazing animals in the whole world. Here are just a few reasons why we love them so much!

1 They give the best cuddles

It's a well-known fact that a cuddle with your fave pony will always make you feel better! Ponies are very intuitive animals and they can tell when you're unhappy and will always try to help cheer you up! Plus, there's no better feeling than having a pony nuzzle up to you.

2 They'll be your BFF

There's something truly magical about being able to completely trust your pony while you're galloping round a cross-country course or cantering along a sandy track. There's nothing else in the world that can compare to the special bond between you.

3 They don't judge

You can tell your pony anything and he won't judge you or gossip behind your back. So long as you give him his dinner every day, he doesn't care what you tell him!

4 They're soooo cute!

All ponies, big or small, are totally adorable. You can snap loads of pics of your fave pony and he'll always look 10/10. Plus, when you're away from your pony BFF, you can spend hours watching funny pony videos.

5 Riding, of course!

When you're riding your pony you feel truly free! Jumping must be what it feels like to have wings and you can spend hours exploring the countryside with him. It's hard to imagine how people without ponies spend their free time!

6 You'll learn loads of things

The lessons you learn from your fave pony are endless. He'll teach you dedication, hard work and patience – especially when he refuses to load into the trailer! But you know all the effort is worth it when you see his happy face peering at you over his stable door.

7 Nothing is impossible

Your fave pony will always try to help you achieve your dreams. Whatever your goal, you can rely on him 100% and he'll never tell you that you can't do something.

8 They make life way better

Riding can help you in all aspects of your life. The confidence your pony gives you will benefit you at school and later in life, too. Above all, it'll show you that you can tackle any problem that comes your way.

Share the love

Make sure you give your fave pony an extra cuddle next time you see him, to show him just how grateful you are that he's part of your world.

QUIZ

LET'S GO HACKING!

Getting out and about with your fave pony is super-fun, but do you know all the hacking dos and don'ts?

1. When should you wear high-vis clothing?

A Every time you go hacking. Your pony should wear some, too

B Only during the winter or if it's raining

C If you're riding on the road

2. You're tacking your pony up ready for a hack – what kit does he need?

A A bright headcollar and some high-vis leg bands

B His bridle, saddle and some high-vis leg bands

C Just his saddle and bridle

3. A car slows down as it drives past you. How do you thank them?

A Nod your head, smile and say "thank you" as they pass

B You don't need to thank them, ponies have right of way on the road

C Smile brightly and wave your whip at them

4. What does this hand signal mean?

A Stop

B Go faster

C I'm turning left

7. **There's a fallen log on your fave hacking route. Do you...**

A Canter up and jump it – wahoo!

B Go round it – you should never jump while on a hack

C Check the take-off and landing sides are safe before popping over it

5. **You're cantering down a bridleway and see a dog walker ahead. Should you...**

A Turn around and go the other way to avoid them

B Slow down to pass them in walk, making sure you give them plenty of room

C Keep cantering, they'll move out of your way

8. **Is it okay for you and a friend to ride side-by-side on the road?**

A Yes, but you should ride in single file along narrow roads and around bends, and to let cars pass

B You should always ride side-by-side because it's much easier to chat

C No, it's best to ride in single file unless you're on a bridleway

6. **Which of these paths shouldn't you ride down?**

A Byway

B Bridleway

C Footpath

9. **What does this sign mean?**

A There might be loose horses in the road because riders often fall off here

B It's warning you that there are wild horses ahead

C You can't ride along this section of road and you have to get off and lead your pony

Turn to page 100 to find out how you got on!

Grooming
MARVELLOUS

Transform your fave pony with these smart grooming tips

Do you want your pony to look amazing for a show, lesson or Pony Club rally? Or would you like to give him a makeover so you can take some super-cute photos? Follow our brilliant tips and you'll be able to turn him out to perfection!

A clean sweep

Grooming your pony every day is the best way to keep him looking clean and tidy. This might not be possible if you're short of time, but it's important to groom him before you ride to remove any dirt or mud that could make his tack uncomfy. Try to give him a more thorough groom after he's been worked, to brush away any grease and dried sweat from his coat.

Pamper your pony

As well as getting your pony looking his best, a head-to-tail grooming session will relax him, and it'll help his skin stay healthy, too. Here's how to give him the five-star treatment...

1. Start by picking out his feet, to remove any dirt and stones and help avoid nasty conditions such as thrush.

2. It's best to work on his mane next, as you'll dislodge dust that'll settle on his coat and undo all your hard work if you've already brushed his body. Spritz it with detangler, then tease out any knots with your fingers or a mane and tail brush.

3. Now remove any dried mud from his coat. Use a dandy brush in short strokes or a rubber curry comb in gentle, circular motions. Don't use a hard brush over bony areas, though, as this'll be uncomfy for him. Tackle muddy legs with a softer-bristled brush, such as a body brush.

4. To lift dust from his coat, hold a body brush in the hand closest to your pony and sweep it over his coat, working from head to tail. Have a metal or plastic curry comb in your other hand and use it to clean the body brush after every few strokes.

5. For the perfect finish, wipe over his coat with a stable rubber or grooming mitt to remove any lingering dust and really make him gleam.

TOP TIP
You won't be able to get your pony sparkling if your brushes are dirty. Wash them in warm, soapy water at least once a month, then leave them to air dry.

DID YOU KNOW?
A body brush can remove natural oils that make your pony's coat waterproof, so avoid using one on a pony that lives out. Use a flick brush to tackle the dust in his coat instead.

DID YOU KNOW?
Tomato ketchup's said to be great at getting stains out of pony's tails! Rub a blob into the lower part of his tail, leave for 5 mins to perform its magic, then rinse out.

Hair today

If you're looking for an easy way to spruce up your pony, just focusing on his mane and tail can make a huge difference in a short time...

1. To wash your pony's mane and tail, make the hair wet, then rub in some shampoo. White tails can become stained and look yellowish, so you might need to apply some stain remover to the bottom to help get it sparkling. Leave it to soak in for a few minutes before rinsing it out.

2. When the hair's dry, apply a few squirts of detangler, tease out any knots, then gently brush it until it's smooth and sleek.

44 Keep on top of stains and deal with them straightaway 🎈

TOP TIP
If you turn your pony out after he's had a bath he'll probably roll, which will undo all your hard work. If you really need him to stay clean, pop a lightweight turnout rug on him.

Stay away stains

Grass and poo stains can be a real pain, especially if your pony's grey. The best thing to do is keep on top of them and deal with them straightaway. If they're left until just before a show it'll be harder to make them disappear. So, either wait until they're dry and brush them out, or squirt with stain remover, rub it in gently using a cloth or sponge, then rinse.

Feet first

Getting your pony's feet wet too often can weaken his hooves, so avoid washing them off every day. If they're muddy, scrape off what you can with a hoof pick, and leave his feet to dry. Then you can gently use a hard-bristled brush to remove the remaining dirt.

Hoof oil will leave his feet gleaming for a show, but it shouldn't be used too often as it can dry hooves out.

Bath time

If you want to get your fave pony squeaky clean, you'll need to give him a bath. Choose a warm day, because it'll be unfair to get him wet if it's cold, and tie him up on the yard with a haynet to munch on.

1. Pour some warm water into a bucket, then use a sponge to wet your pony's coat.
2. Squirt a pea-sized blob of shampoo onto the sponge and rub it into his coat to create a frothy lather. Work from his head to his tail, adding more shampoo to the sponge as you need it, and making sure you don't miss anywhere. Don't forget to include his mane and tail, too.
3. After shampooing your pony, you'll need to rinse out all the bubbles. Use clean water and again work from his head to his tail, until his hair's soap free.
4. A sweat scraper will remove any excess water and help your pony dry off more quickly. Place the scraper against his coat and slide it over the hair, using gentle pressure to squeeze the water out.
5. You can pop a drying or cooler rug on him until he's completely dry.

TOP TIP
Ask your farrier whether your pony's feet would benefit from a conditioning product to help keep them strong and healthy.

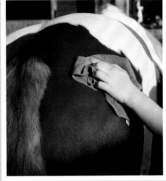

TOP TIP

It's quicker to rinse shampoo out using a hosepipe, as long as your pony doesn't mind this and it's a warm enough day. Keep the pipe well clear of his legs and have the water at a steady trickle.

Regularly grooming your pony will make it easier to get him looking smart for shows

Make him shine

If it's too chilly to bath your pony there's a handy trick you can use to get him clean and shiny! Hot clothing involves using a damp cloth to bring dust and grease to the surface, and it's really easy to do. You'll need a flannel or a square cut from an old towel and a bucket of water that's hot, but not so hot that you can't comfortably put your hand in. Some people also add a few drops of baby oil or coat shine to the water.

1. Dip your cloth into the hot water, then ring it out so it's damp but not wet.
2. Wipe the cloth over your pony's coat, using a small amount of pressure to lift the dirt.
3. After every three or four sweeps of his coat, rinse the cloth out. Dip it in the hot water again before squeezing out the excess and tackling the next section of his body.

TOP TIP

Hot clothing is a brilliant way to get clipped ponies gleaming.

The FOOD FACTORY

Take a journey through your pony's digestive system to find out how food travels from his mouth to the muck heap!

Most ponies love munching, and eating the right food is super-important. It'll give him energy to fuel his ridden work, supply him with the nutrients he needs to stay healthy, and help keep him warm, too! Here's how your pony's food takes an incredible journey through his body to do all of these things.

Making waves
The chewed up food travels down the **oesophagus**, a 1m long tube which makes a wave-like motion to push it down into his stomach.

Chew, chew!
Your pony's **mouth** is where it all begins! He uses his lips to gather in grass, hay or hard feed, then his teeth grind it down into small particles. As the food's swirled around in his mouth by his tongue, it gets mixed with saliva so it's easier to swallow.

DID YOU KNOW?
It can take 24 hours for food to go all the way through your pony's digestive system!

DID YOU KNOW?
The most important food your pony eats is fibre, such as grass, hay, haylage and chaff. He should eat approx 1.5-2% of his bodyweight in fibre each day.

TOP TIP
Sharp teeth are not only painful for your pony, they make it hard for him to chew his food properly. Have his teeth checked at least once a year by a your vet or a qualified equine dental technician.

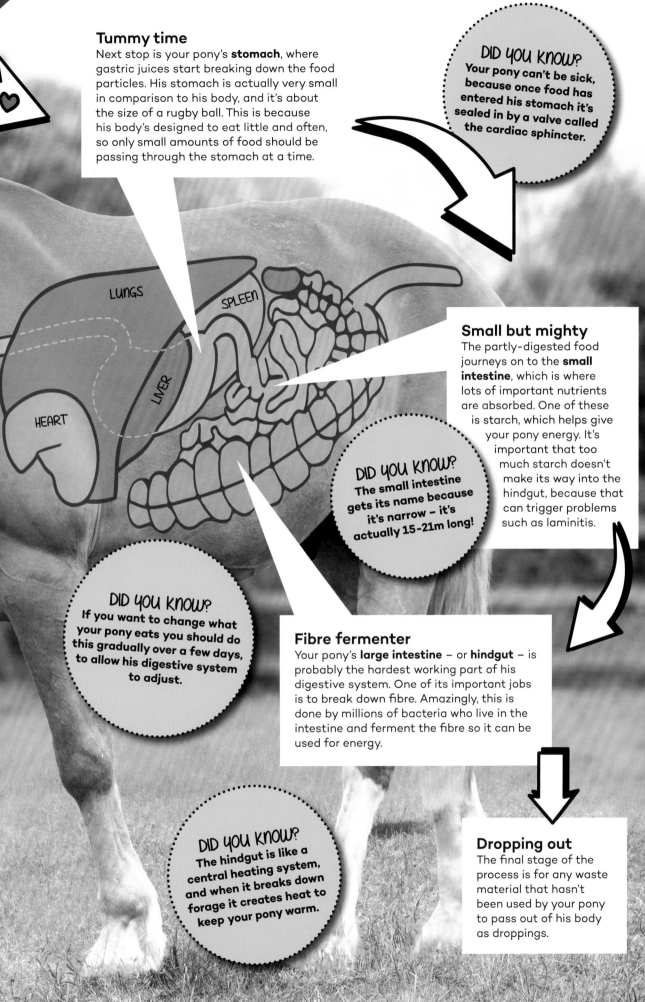

Tummy time

Next stop is your pony's **stomach**, where gastric juices start breaking down the food particles. His stomach is actually very small in comparison to his body, and it's about the size of a rugby ball. This is because his body's designed to eat little and often, so only small amounts of food should be passing through the stomach at a time.

DID YOU KNOW?
Your pony can't be sick, because once food has entered his stomach it's sealed in by a valve called the cardiac sphincter.

LUNGS

SPLEEN

LIVER

HEART

Small but mighty

The partly-digested food journeys on to the **small intestine**, which is where lots of important nutrients are absorbed. One of these is starch, which helps give your pony energy. It's important that too much starch doesn't make its way into the hindgut, because that can trigger problems such as laminitis.

DID YOU KNOW?
The small intestine gets its name because it's narrow – it's actually 15-21m long!

DID YOU KNOW?
If you want to change what your pony eats you should do this gradually over a few days, to allow his digestive system to adjust.

Fibre fermenter

Your pony's **large intestine** – or **hindgut** – is probably the hardest working part of his digestive system. One of its important jobs is to break down fibre. Amazingly, this is done by millions of bacteria who live in the intestine and ferment the fibre so it can be used for energy.

DID YOU KNOW?
The hindgut is like a central heating system, and when it breaks down forage it creates heat to keep your pony warm.

Dropping out

The final stage of the process is for any waste material that hasn't been used by your pony to pass out of his body as droppings.

SPOT ON

These brilliant exercises will improve your accuracy so you become a better rider

Do you want to know the secret to being an amazing rider? It's trying to be as accurate as possible, whether that's making sure your pony responds as soon as you ask him to do something, or always riding super-straight lines or perfectly round circles. Accuracy is important for loads of reasons. As well as helping you ride better, your pony will understand exactly what you expect of him, and you'll get waaaay higher marks if you compete in dressage tests! Luckily, it's something that's super-easy to work on, and these fun exercises will help!

Exercise 1
READY TO RESPOND

Being accurate starts with making sure your fave pony's super-obedient to your aids, so he moves forward, slows down or stops as soon as you ask him to. Not only will it make him more enjoyable to ride, you'll find it easier to perfect school shapes, too.

Set up
You don't need any special equipment for this exercise and you can try it in an arena, in a field or even out hacking!

How to ride it
1. Start in halt, with plenty of space in front of you so you can ride forward. Sit up tall with your shoulders back and have a soft, even contact with your pony's mouth.
2. Give him a gentle squeeze with your legs and allow him a moment to respond. If he steps forward that's great, but if he doesn't give him a slightly stronger squeeze with your legs. Repeat the stronger aid until he walks on.
3. Ride straight for five or six strides, then bring him back to halt by sitting up tall, putting more weight on your seat bones and gently squeezing the reins. If it takes him a few strides to come to a halt, don't worry, as it's something that'll improve with practice. Give him a scratch on his neck to let him know he's done the right thing.
4. Count to three then walk on for a few strides before halting again. If you repeat the halt-walk-halt transitions a few times, you should soon find that you're getting an instant response from your pony.
5. Now try the exercise again, but going from walk to trot, then trot to walk.

Up the challenge
Ride the transitions closer together, so walk for three strides, then trot for three and so on. This is a great way to get your pony thinking forward and make his paces more energetic.

Exercise 2
STRAIGHT AND NARROW

Being able to ride perfectly straight lines is super-important if you want to compete in dressage or jumping, but it'll also make sure you work your pony's body evenly and he doesn't become crooked and sore in his muscles. You can practise this by using poles to guide you.

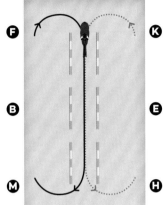

Set up
Create a channel of poles down the centre line, approx 1-2m apart. This exercise will only work if the poles are really straight, so if you're not sure, ask an adult to help you.

How to ride it
1. Turn down the centre line at A and ride between the poles. Make sure you're sitting evenly in the saddle, wrap your legs around your pony's sides and have an equal contact in your reins. Looking up and ahead to the C marker will help stop you wobbling.
2. When you're feeling confident in walk, have a go in trot.
3. Now widen the channel of poles, so they're still there as a guide, but you're relying on them a bit less.
4. Remove the poles completely and see how straight you are!

TOP TIP
Make sure you're not doing something that's making your pony crooked, such as leaning to one side or giving a stronger aid with one rein or leg.

TOP TIP
Get a friend to stand at C to check you're straight. Or ask them to film you, so you can see for yourself!

TOP TIP
Plan your turn onto the centre line to help you keep straight. Aim to ride a smooth, balanced turn that will give you the best chance of staying straight all the way from A-C.

Exercise 3
ALL SQUARE

You probably ride more 20m circles than any other shape, but can you honestly say they're always perfectly round and the right size? This exercise makes you think about riding a square, but it'll actually help you ace 20m circles every time!

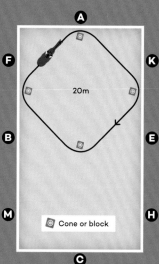

20m

Cone or block

Set up
Use four cones or blocks to mark out a 20m square. Place them at A and X, and 10m in from the corner between F and B and K and E. Make sure the markers are just in from the track, so there's room to ride around them.

How to ride it
1. In walk, ride from marker to marker to create a square. To keep your pony straight on the four sides, sit evenly in the saddle, have an equal contact on the reins and look up and ahead between his ears.
2. As you approach the first marker, prepare for the turn by sitting up tall, gently squeezing the reins and wrapping your legs around his sides. This'll make sure he's

focused on you and help him keep his balance.
3. Open your inside hand a little, but don't pull him round – instead, guide him through the turn using your outside aids. Push him round with your outside rein against his neck, and your outside leg just behind the girth to support his quarters. Press your inside leg on the girth to ask him to bend.
4. Ride round the four markers, then change the rein.
5. Gradually turn your square into a rounder shape by riding curves rather than corners, but continue to use your outside aids to turn.
6. Have a go in trot.
7. Remove the cones and see if you can ride an accurate circle without them.

TOP TIP
If your arena has mirrors, you can look in them to check your school shapes are accurate, or ask your instructor to watch you ride.

Exercise 4
CLASSY CORNERS

Corners are important because they help your pony's bend and suppleness, and they rebalance him and prepare him for what movement you'll be riding next. But loads of riders cut across them or whizz through them too fast. This cone exercise will help you to ride them correctly.

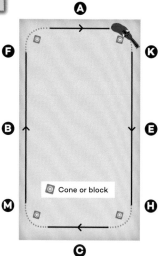

Cone or block

Set up
Place a cone or block approx 1.5m inside each arena corner.

How to ride it
1. Go large in walk and approach the first corner. Make sure your pony's listening to you by sitting up tall, squeezing the reins and wrapping your legs around his sides.
2. As you come into the corner, open your inside rein slightly and press your inside leg against the girth to ask him to bend around the marker. Support his quarters

by placing your outside leg behind the girth, and guide his head by holding your outside rein against his neck.
3. Ride a smooth curve around the cone.
4. Once you've ridden four corners, change the rein and try the exercise in the opposite direction.
5. Remove the markers one at a time, and gradually build up to riding all four corners without a guide. Focus on riding deep into each one.

TOP TIP
To help you ride a corner, think of it as a quarter of a circle.

TOP TIP
You don't need to try all of these exercises at once, but even doing one or two each time you ride will make a big difference.

TOP TIP
Using stripey poles will help you aim for the middle.

Exercise 5
STAY ON COURSE

Accuracy is important in jumping, too, and you should always aim for the middle of a fence. You don't need to jump loads to practise this, and working over ground poles is super-useful.

How to ride it
1. Place five or six poles on the ground to create a course.
2. Walk your pony over the poles one at a time, aiming for the middle.
3. Have a go in trot, then mix things up by changing the order you ride over them.
4. Pop your pony into canter, and focus on keeping a rhythm around the course, while still making sure you ride over the centre of the poles.

Up the challenge
You can turn the poles into small fences, but keep things low and easy for your pony.

Exercise 6
THE RIGHT LINES

Approaching a fence on a super-straight line gives your pony the best chance of clearing it. But remember that he should stay straight on landing, too, so you can prepare him properly for the next fence on the course.

Set up
Build a small, easy fence in an arena or field, such as a low cross-pole. Place ground poles on the take-off and landing sides to keep you straight. If you have enough poles and wings, you could build a second fence four or five strides from the first one.

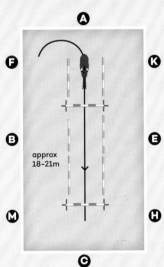

approx 18-21m

How to ride it
1. Go large around the arena in trot and plan your approach to the fence. Look up to where you want to go, then make a smooth turn into your channel of poles.
2. Sit up as soon as you land, then ride forward and straight to your next fence.
3. Ride through the exercise again, this time approaching on the other rein.

QUIZ
UNIQUE UNICORNS

Is your fave pony a Fire, Earth, Air or Water Unicorn? Complete the quiz to find out!

Did you know that all ponies are secretly unicorns? Also, there are four types of this magical creature – Fire, Earth, Air and Water – and knowing which your pony is will help you better understand his character. Read on to discover your fave pony's unicorn name and personality.

FIRE EARTH AIR WATER

NAME GAME

To discover your fave pony's unicorn name, take the first letter of his name and his birth month, then use the chart below! For example, if your fave pony's called Monkey and he was born in December, his unicorn name will be Mysterious Twinkle Toes. If you're not sure when his birthday is, use your own.

His initial letter

A) Magical	**N)** Jazzy
B) Rainbow	**O)** Silvery
C) Fluffy	**P)** Prancing
D) Glitter	**Q)** Awesome
E) Shimmer	**R)** Fabulous
F) Sunny	**S)** Dazzling
G) Secret	**T)** Galloping
H) Dream	**U)** Starlight
I) Mystic	**V)** Ruby
J) Dancing	**W)** Bubble
K) Enchanted	**X)** Glitzy
L) Sprinkle	**Y)** Sky
M) Mysterious	**Z)** Bright

His birth month

Jan	Periwinkle	**Jul**	Onyx
Feb	Moonstone	**Aug**	Star
Mar	Sparkle	**Sept**	Topaz
Apr	Emerald	**Oct**	Sapphire
May	Gold	**Nov**	Truffle
Jun	Amethyst	**Dec**	Twinkle Toes

UNICORN NAME

Darwin   Mac
Glitter Star Mysterious Sparkle
me: Magical Start

LET'S GET QUIZZICAL!

Now it's time to find out what type of unicorn he is – Fire, Earth, Air or Water!

1. **You're out on a hack with your fave pony and you come to the perfect canter track? Does he...**

A Immediately try to speed up – he wants to gallop!

B Keep going at the same pace and wait for you to decide what to do.

C Have a small spook to check you're paying attention.

D Wait to see what the other ponies do, then copy them.

2. **What magical unicorn power do you wish your pony had?**

A Flying

B Wish granting

C Teleporting

D Invisibility

3. **What's your pony's fave activity?**

A Going as fast as he can.

B Having a snooze.

C Being involved in whatever's happening on the yard.

D Spending time with his friends.

4. **What word would you use to describe your fave pony?**

A Active

B Reliable

C Clever

D Sociable

5. **What's your pony's least fave discipline?**

A Dressage, it's sooo boring.

B Nothing! He loves everything you try together.

C Showjumping – he hates all the spooky fillers.

D Mounted games, because there's too many things going on.

6. **What's your pony's fave treat**

A Mints, especially Polos.

B Anything, he loooooves food!

C He only eats homemade treats.

D Apples or carrots.

7. **You've decided to take your fave pony to a local show. What class do you enter?**

A Showjumping – he'll ace the jump-off.

B Handy pony – he's amazing at obstacle courses.

C A showing class – the judges always love his good looks.

D Dressage – he's got flashy paces, plus it's your fave discipline.

Turn to page 100 to find out what type of unicorn he is!

MOVING ON

Ziggy finds fitting in at his new yard harder than he expected

I've lived with a few families, but it still came as a bit of a shock when I released that my current owner, Victoria, was planning to sell me. We'd had a great few years together, but I suppose she was starting to get a bit tall for me.

Different people turned up to see me, but they didn't feel like quite the right fit. Finally a girl with a kind smile and soft voice came. I liked her immediately and kept my hooves crossed that she'd like me, too.

On my way

I was thrilled when the nice girl came back to ride me a second time, and it went so well that I thought she might be my new rider. She was back again a few days later with her mum and dad to pick me up. Victoria had already put on my travelling kit when the trailer arrived, and when she opened the door to my stable she put her arms around my neck and gave me a squeeze.

"Be a good boy for Ava, Ziggy," she mumbled into my neck, and I could feel a growing wet patch from her tears. "I love you, boy." I nudged her with my nose and let out a small whicker, hoping she'd understand that I loved her, too.

Victoria walked me onto the trailer, gave me one last kiss, then the ramp was closed and soon I was on my way to my new home. I couldn't help but feel a little nervous. What would Ava be like? Would I make friends with the ponies at the new yard?

First impressions

When we arrived at the yard, the front ramp was slowly lowered and I could see a neat stable block with large green fields behind it. Ava walked up the ramp and gave me pat.

"Here we are, Ziggy," she said as she led me out and onto the yard. There were stables on either side of me and I spotted a few ponies watching us. When we reached the end of the yard, Ava tied me up next to a stable. She took off my travel boots, gave me a groom and then put me into the stable. After a quick look round my new space, I popped my head over the door and neighed loudly.

"Shhh! No need to shout," I heard a reply from my left. I swung my head round to look for the pony. "The new ones always shout, it's so annoying." The voice belonged to a very beautiful palomino mare in the

Would I make friends with the ponies at my new yard?

stable next door. "I'm sorry, I'm just a bit nervous!" I explained, eager to make a friend. "My name's Ziggy, what's it like here? Ava, my new human, seems nice." The pony looked at me and snorted. "Just wait and see," she replied mysteriously, before disappearing back inside her stable.

A new day

I barely got any sleep that night. There were loads of strange noises, and it was hard to drift off not really knowing where I was. So, I was excited to see Ava when she arrived early the next morning to give me my breakfast. After I'd eaten she turned me out into a small paddock next to some other ponies and I trotted straight over to the fence to introduce myself.

"Hi everyone! I just got here, I'm Ziggy, it's nice to meet you..." I was interrupted by the same pony I'd met the night before. "Are you ever quiet?" she snapped at me, tossing her mane with irritation. "We know you're new, we saw you arrive. Come on guys, let's go." She turned tail and led the small herd of ponies across to the other side of their field, where they stayed for the rest of the day.

I couldn't understand what I'd done to upset her, I only wanted to make friends. The day passed by slowly with nobody to talk to, and I missed my old yard. It was a bit of a relief when Ava arrived to catch me, and I trotted straight over to the gate to greet her.

"Hey, Ziggy," she laughed when I whinnied in reply. She took me back to the yard for another groom and a few apples, too.

Feeling lonely

Every day was the same, with the other ponies ignoring me, and by the end of my first week I still hadn't managed to make any friends. Then, a Shetland pony was tied up next to me while Ava was grooming me after our ride. I glanced over at him, but didn't dare ask any questions, afraid of being ignored.

"Don't worry about Goldie," he suddenly said in a deep voice. "She's just jealous, she'll come round." I turned my head to stare at him. "Why would she be jealous of me?" I asked. I've only just got here!"

"Goldie used to be Ava's pony, but Ava's too big for her now. She's upset because Ava doesn't ride her any more, even though she's got a new owner that loves

her loads," the pony explained. "I'm Dave, by the way."
"Nice to meet you, I'm Ziggy," I replied, as my brain raced with this new information. How could I convince Goldie that Ava still has time for her, too? I spent the rest of the evening thinking about ways to make friends with her.

On a mission

The next morning the ponies in the other field continued to graze as far away from me as they could. This time I wasn't worried, because I had a plan to get Goldie to talk to me.

I stayed near the fence all day, as close to the others as I could. Then, when Ava came to catch me, I didn't trot over to her, and she had to come over to fetch me. I kept my focus on Goldie while Ava chatted to me quietly, and just before she slipped my headcollar on I danced away.

"Come on Ziggy, let's go," Ava said in her soft voice, offering me a treat from her pocket. But I continued to stay just out of reach. "What are you doing?" came Goldie's voice from over the fence and I watched as she walked over towards my paddock. "Good boy, Ziggy, please let me catch you!" Ava coaxed, walking towards me with the treat in her hand. By this time Goldie was standing by the fence watching us. Ava noticed her immediately, and went over to give her a fuss and a treat.

"Hi, gorgeous girl," Ava cooed as she gently stroked Goldie's neck. "She can like both of us you know," I said quietly to Goldie as I walked towards the pair. "She hasn't forgotten about you just because I'm here." Goldie's nostrils flared in surprise. "It's just hard to accept she's got a new pony. She used to spend all her time with me," she explained. Ava gave Goldie a gentle

kiss on the nose, then slowly approached me again. I eagerly accepted the treat from her hand and let her put my headcollar on.

"I know Ava's got time for both of us. Plus, I'd love to hear all about her, I'm sure you've got loads of advice," I tried to reassure Goldie. "I'll think about it," was the only response I got as Ava led me away to my stable.

Friends at last

Goldie was waiting for me by the fence when I got to the field the next day.

"I've thought about it and I want you and Ava to have a good partnership. I want her to be happy," she said, looking down at her hooves. "So, I'll tell you about her." I couldn't believe she'd changed her mind. "Thank you, Goldie!" I said sincerely. She spent the rest of the day telling me stories about Ava and everything they'd done together. I was having so much fun I didn't want to leave when Ava came to catch me.

As soon as Goldie came in from the field that evening, I told her all about my old yard and she gushed about her new rider, Charlotte. We ended up chatting all night! I finally felt like I'd made a friend and even though I stayed in a separate paddock for another week, Goldie continued to graze by the fence so we could chat, and I started to make friends with the other ponies in the herd, too.

Best friends forever

Goldie's become my best friend and we can usually be found grazing side by side. Ava always keeps an extra treat in her pocket for Goldie when she comes to catch me, and thanks to Goldie's tips I've been having loads of fun with Ava, too! It really feels like I've finally settled into my new life with Ava and Goldie.

Kentucky
HORSE TRIALS

Find out why Kentucky is one of the most famous horse trials in the world

The Land Rover Kentucky Horse Trials takes place in the USA each spring and it's super-exciting for loads of reasons. It's the world's first major three-day event of the year, so all eyes are on the riders and horses to see who's going to get the new season off to the best start. Plus, it's one of three events that make up the famous Rolex Grand Slam, and the winner could be in line for a huge bonus prize if they also top the leaderboard at Badminton and Burghley.

DID YOU KNOW?
The horse trials is held at Kentucky Horse Park, which is an equine theme park! It attracts 1 million visitors a year, and from April to October you can tour the Hall of Champions, watch a Parade of Breeds and even go on a trail ride!

DID YOU KNOW?
Kentucky Horse Park hosted the World Equestrian Games in 2010, which was the first time the event was held outside Europe!

Save the date
The 2020 event takes place from 23-26 April.

USA

Location, location, location
The horse trials' venue, Kentucky Horse Park, is steeped in equestrian heritage. It's in Lexington, a city that's known as the equestrian capital of the world because of its connection to horses and the racing industry. There are around 400 horse farms in the area!

THE COMPETITION

Just like the UK's Badminton and Burghley Horse Trials, Kentucky is a three-day event and riders take part in dressage, cross-country and showjumping. It's classed as a five-star competition, which means it's the highest level of eventing. There are only five other five-star horse trials in the world – Badminton, Burghley, Luhmühlen in Germany, Pau in France and Adelaide in Australia.

Alongside the eventing, there's loads of other entertainment for spectators to enjoy, such as dressage demos, mounted games and breed displays. Plus, there's a chance to treat yourself to something special from the shopping village!

Brits abroad

Riders from Great Britain have made the long journey to Kentucky well worth it in recent years. Oliver Townend has won the last two events, both on Cooley Master Class. Badminton winner Piggy French made 2019 super-successful by coming fourth at Kentucky.

Another famous British rider, William Fox-Pitt, lifted the Kentucky trophy three times between 2010 and 2014.

The magic number

The Rolex Grand Slam of Eventing is an exciting challenge laid down to event riders – if they win Badminton, Burghley and Kentucky they'll receive an extra prize of $350,000 (around £270,000)! The wins can be on different horses, but they must happen consecutively (one after the other).

This is no mean feat and in the 21 years since The Grand Slam was launched only two riders have achieved it – Pippa Funnell in 2003 and Michael Jung in 2015/2016.

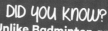
Oliver Townend

Piggy French

PERCHERON

A perfect combination of strength, beauty and grace, these versatile horses excel in riding and driving

DID YOU KNOW?
Many Percherons have Thoroughbred, Arab and Andalusion breeding somewhere in their bloodlines, which makes them more athletic than other draught horses.

One of the gentle giants of the horse world, Percherons are popular because of their willing nature and versatility. Once used as a war horse, they're equally comfortable turning their hooves to all types of work under saddle or in harness.

History

This powerhouse is one of the oldest draught breeds in the world, and is thought to trace back as far as AD 732! It's believed that they first came to Britain from France in 1066 with William the Conqueror when he travelled to invade England. It wasn't until the late 19th Century that they became more popular in Britain, though. They were imported from America to pull London buses and fire engines.

Despite being a firm favourite with so many people, there are only around 300 registered pure-bred Percherons in Britain today.

FACT FILE

HEIGHT: Mares must be at least 16.1hh, while geldings and stallions are slightly taller and at least 16.2hh by two years of age.

COLOUR: While Percherons across the world can be black, grey, chestnut, bay or roan, in Britain the studbook requires them to be black or grey. They're usually born black, then their coat lightens as they get older.

PLACE OF ORIGIN: Le Perche, a province of Normandy, France.

KNOWN FOR: Their intelligence, sturdiness, willingness to work, docile nature and placid temperament.

War horse

With no feather or long hair on their legs, the Percheron was much lower-maintenance than some of their more feathered friends, such as the Clydesdale, and this made them well-suited to the dirty, muddy conditions of war.

The breed's willingness and laid-back nature meant they became super-popular with soldiers. As well as being easy to keep, they were calm and quiet to handle, even mid-battle when lots of frightening things were going on around them. This was really important because often the soldiers had never ridden before, and needed to learn on the job!

DID YOU KNOW?
Percherons are often described as cold-blooded. This is nothing to do with temperature, and actually describes their calm, quiet temperament.

DID YOU KNOW?
The British Percheron Horse Society was set up in 1918, and in the four years following this, 184 stallions and 321 mares were imported from France.

Spot the difference

The breed is super-popular in the US, too, but there are differences between British European and US types. Generally, American and Canadian Percherons are slightly less stocky and sportier-looking, as well as being taller. They're also mostly black in colour, rather than the grey that's preferred in the UK.

DID YOU KNOW?
If you've ever been to Disneyland Paris or Disney World, you've probably seen a Percheron. The teams of horses that pull trams around the parks are normally Percherons.

Jack of all trades

The Percheron has been the top choice of many horse owners for loads of reasons – they're calm, hard-working and well-muscled. Because of their kind nature, they're one of the best breeds for adults who are new to riding.

They've had a variety of jobs over the years, and as well as working on farms and serving in the war, they've made successful police horses. They're elegant and graceful enough to be used as carriage horses, too.

Showing stars

In 2017, Horse of the Year Show launched the British Ridden Heavy Horse of the Year championship. In this class, Percherons compete against other breeds such as Shires, Clydesdales and Suffolk Punches. The winner of the first ever class was Percheron Hales Hector, ridden by Household Cavalry rider Jamie Bradbury.

"The most important thing is that you enjoy yourself"

SAY NO TO NERVES

Don't let being nervous spoil your riding fun. Check out these 12 brilliant ways to be super-confident

Even if your fave thing ever is riding and spending time with ponies, it's still possible to feel nervous or anxious when you're around them. What you need to remember is that nerves are perfectly normal and are something that can affect anyone, even top riders! The good news is there's loads you can do to ease the butterflies in your tummy and feel super-confident!

How nerves affect your riding

It's important to find a way to overcome nerves so they don't spoil your fun or affect your riding. If you're feeling anxious, you'll tense up and you might tip forward, grip with your legs or hold the reins tightly. These can all be uncomfy for your pony and, as well as making him less willing to go forward, he'll start to think there's something he should be worried about, too.

1 Share your worries

Whatever you're nervous or worried about, the best thing to do is talk to your instructor and let them know how you're feeling. They'll totally understand and will be used to helping riders overcome a confidence crisis. As well as reassuring you, they'll be able to suggest helpful things you can try, too. So, speak to them before your next lesson or, if you'd find this tricky, ask one of your parents to call them.

TOP TIP
If you usually have group lessons, why not see if you can book a few individual sessions with your instructor. Then you can really concentrate on your confidence issues.

2 Ride... and repeat

You might find something scary, such as hacking or jumping, because you don't do it very often. So, the answer is to get out there and experience it! If you try to hack or jump two or three times a week, it'll soon become a normal thing that you enjoy with your pony! Always keep things simple to start with, though, such as going for short hacks with a friend on an experienced, calm pony, and build up your jumping confidence by booking some extra lessons and starting with easy polework exercises.

3

Dress for success

Having the proper kit for riding should help you feel safer, which will boost your confidence. As well as wearing an up-to-standard riding hat, consider wearing a body protector, too. You can also invest in an air jacket, which will inflate to cushion your landing if you part company with your pony.

TOP TIP

A neckstrap can help you feel more secure in the saddle. You can use an old stirrup leather – just fasten it round your pony's neck and slip your fingers through it if you feel nervous.

4

Find your pony super hero

The pony you ride can make a huge difference to your confidence levels, and if he's spooky or strong it's no wonder you're worried. But, find one that you trust 100%, and you'll feel like you can do anything together!

Even teaming up with a super-safe pony for a short time can change the way you feel about riding and help you progress much more quickly. You can book some lessons at a riding school on a schoolmaster or talk to your instructor about your options. They may know the perfect pony that you could have a few lessons on or borrow to help restore your confidence.

5

Feel good vibes only

Staying positive can help you feel waaay more confident, and you'll enjoy your pony time loads more. So, try not to always expect the worst or constantly think about something that didn't go well in the past. Instead, tell yourself "I can do this" or "I've had a go at this before and I really enjoyed it". You're sure to find that your pony picks up on your positive mood, and is more relaxed around you, too.

6 Try some confidence tricks

There are loads of tried and tested ways to boost your confidence, so why not give these ideas a try?

● **focus on your breathing**
Breathe in through your nose, then out through your mouth in a gentle rhythm to help you feel calmer

● **block out the bad thoughts**
Keep your brain busy thinking about other things, so you don't leave any room for negative thoughts! So, if you find yourself starting to worry about your dressage test or jumping round, think about keeping your heels down instead, and you'll find those bad thoughts will disappear

● **imagine being amazing**
Visualisation is a technique the world's best riders use. Before they compete they'll go through their dressage test or showjumping round in their mind and imagine themselves doing it perfectly. They'll then ride into the arena feeling that they're going to ace the challenge ahead of them

7 Rehearse in front of friends

Competition nerves are really common, and they often surface because you're worried about having to ride in front of other people. The secret is to really focus on yourself and your pony and what you need to do in your class, then you'll soon forget about everyone else. Another thing you can do is get some friends together at the yard and let them watch you practising your dressage test or schooling over jumps. You may find that you love showing off what your pony can do to an audience!

TOP TIP
When trying something new, always keep things easy at first and build up gradually.

8 Release the pressure

If you're taking your fave pony to a show you're sure to want to do well, but don't put lots of pressure on yourself by making it all about winning a prize. This is a sure-fire way to feel nervous! Instead, keep the focus on spending quality time with your pony and putting what you've learned at home to the test. Why not give yourself a personal goal to aim for instead, such as riding the best possible centre line, or keeping a forward canter rhythm around the fences? It'll help you think and ride more positively, so it'll actually increase the chances of you doing well! Then, if you do win or get placed, it'll be an added bonus.

9 Be prepared

Top riders leave no stone unturned in the days before a show. If you do the same you'll have the confidence that you've done everything you can to ensure the day runs smoothly. So, make sure you and your pony are ready for your class by putting in lots of practice and having some extra lessons with your instructor.

10 Don't forget to eat

If your tummy's doing backflips, food might be the last thing you want to think about, but if you don't eat anything, you won't have enough energy to ride properly. Even if you're not hungry, try to snack on something healthy, such as fruit or a handful of nuts, and make sure you drink lots of water, too.

TOP TIP
It's really common to hold your breath when you're nervous. You can stop yourself doing this by singing or counting out loud!

11 Get plenty of sleep

Sleep is super-important, so have a relaxing bath and aim to get an early night before a show or any other important day. If you're properly rested you'll feel refreshed and ready to take on anything.

12 Enjoy yourself

Whatever you do with your pony, the most important thing is to have fun. So, focus on the great memories you're creating, which will make it all the more rewarding, and it'll help ease any worries you have, too!

QUIZ

STAR TREATMENT

Can you help Emily care for her friend Katie's pony, Star, while she's away for the weekend?

1. **Emily's first job of the day is to lead Star in from the field, so he can eat his breakfast. What does she need to take with her?**

   Star's headcollar and leadrope.

   A bucket of nuts – if she rattles them, Star's sure to follow.

   Just a leadrope, as she can place it around his neck to lead him.

2. **After Star's eaten, Emily ties him up on the yard to give him a groom. What should she do first?**

   Brush through his tail.

   Pick out his feet to remove any dirt and debris.

   Wash his white socks.

3. **Star lives out and his coat is covered in dried mud. What's the best brush to use to clean him up?**

   Body brush

   Dandy brush

   Face brush

4. **What else can Emily do while she's grooming Star?**

   Check him over carefully to make sure he doesn't have any cuts, grazes or bumps.

   Sing to him – it helps him relax.

   Spray him all over with coat shine so he gleams.

5. **It's going to be a sunny day and Star's sensitive to insects, so what does he need to go back out in the field?**

   Nothing, he'll enjoy the feeling of the sun on his back.

   A warm turnout rug, just in case it turns cold later.

   A fly rug and mask, plus a squirt of fly repellent.

6. **Before Emily leaves the yard, what final checks should she make?**

 That Star has plenty of water and the fencing in his paddock is secure.

 None – she needs to hurry as her mum's waiting for her.

That Star's tack is clean, ready for when Katie's back from her hols.

7. **While she's in Star's field, Emily notices a strange plant in the field. She thinks it could be ragwort – what should she do?**

 Pull it up straightaway, even though she isn't wearing gloves.

 Don't worry about it as someone else will spot it.

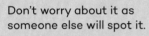 Go and find the yard manager, and show them where the plant is so they can remove it safely.

8. **When Emily comes back to the yard in the afternoon, she remembers that Katie asked her to poo-pick Star's paddock. What can she do with the muck?**

Put it in a wheelbarrow and empty it onto the muck heap.

Fling it over the hedge

Hide it in the next paddock.

9. **The weather forecast says it's going to be warm overnight, but there could be showers, so Emily decides to pop a rug on Star. Which is the best one to use?**

 A cooler rug – if he gets wet it'll help him dry off really quickly.

 A lightweight rain sheet – it'll keep him dry, but he won't get too hot.

 A stable rug – then she won't have to change it if she decides to put him in the stable next morning.

10. **To do Star's rug change Emily should...**

 Change the rugs in his field. If he trots off, she'll just have to run alongside him.

Catch him, but tie him to the gate to save time.

 Catch him and bring him to the yard, so she can tie him up safely while she changes his rugs.

Turn to page 100 to find out how you got on!

MAKE

a pony pencil topper

A cute way to decorate your pencils and pens

You'll need...

- ✓ Thin, coloured card
- ✓ Scissors
- ✓ Glue
- ✓ Sticky tape
- ✓ Pens or pencils
- ✓ Stick-on gems

TOP TIP
Why not make a stable of pony pencil toppers, with each one in a different colour?

TOP TIP
You can use the same piece of card for the whole pencil topper, or choose a different colour for the mane and forelock.

1. Trace the templates, then cut them out and draw around them on a piece of card.

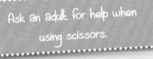

Ask an adult for help when using scissors.

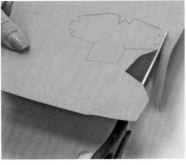

2. Carefully cut out the pony's head, making sure you cut along all the bold lines shown on the template. Then cut out the ears, mane and forelock and put these to pieces to one side.

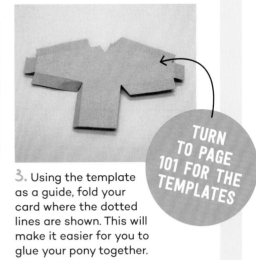

3. Using the template as a guide, fold your card where the dotted lines are shown. This will make it easier for you to glue your pony together.

TURN TO PAGE 101 FOR THE TEMPLATES

4. Curl the neck of your paper pony around your pencil. Carefully position him so the top of the pencil's a few millimetres below the top of his head. Then secure his neck with tape.

5. Next, put a blob of glue on the nose tabs and press them together. Glue the top and bottom of the head in the same way. Make sure you tuck the corners of each tab into your topper, so your pony looks flawless!

6. Carefully glue the ears in place. Don't forget to fold the ears up, to make your pony look alert and happy!

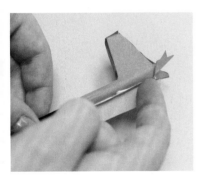

7. Dab some glue on the tab that runs along the mane and attach it to your pony's neck. Don't worry if it's too long, you can always trim it later! Now take the forelock and secure it between the ears.

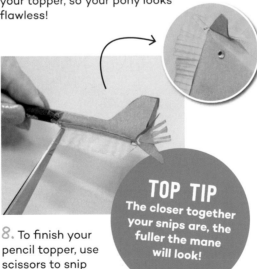

8. To finish your pencil topper, use scissors to snip into the mane and forelock, so they look more like hair. Then add a gem to create your pony's eye!

TOP TIP
The closer together your snips are, the fuller the mane will look!

TA-DAH!

LEARNING TO SHARE

When Keira gets a sharer for her pony, things don't quite go smoothly

Mum says we've got to find a sharer for Munchie. She doesn't think I'll have enough time to ride him with my exams coming up.

I suppose so, I've got someone coming to try him tomorrow.

That was quick!

That sounds like a good idea, they'll be able to help you keep him fit.

If you decide to share him, you'll be totally responsible for him three days a week, including riding.

Rose and her mum watch Keira ride Munchie.

Wow Mum, he looks amazing

Okay, that would be fab.

Jemima, he's amazing! I just had the best jumping lesson on him.

I'd love to share him if that's okay with you?

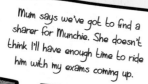

NEXT WEEK...

Absolutely, I think you'll get on really well together.

Oh, hey Rose! Are you enjoying sharing Munchie?

Cara and Peaches as **Jemima and Orange**

Emma as **Rose**

Megan and Rupert as **Keira and Munchie**

PONY FESS UPS

If ponies could talk here are some confessions they might share

THAT'S SO FUNNY!

Kinda cringe

Whoops!

Soooo cringe!

CRINGE-O-METER

Out of buck
It had been ages since my owner, Ollie, and I had gone for a long hack, and when we reached our fave canter track I couldn't help but do a happy little buck. It turns out that Ollie was daydreaming and he fell off – oops! I was sooo embarrassed, but luckily he saw the funny side and we had a mega canter afterwards.

Zippy

Itchy scratchy

I was tied up on the yard while my rider, Cara, was getting me ready for a show, when suddenly my ear felt really itchy. I started to rub it on the closet thing I could – a stable door – forgetting that I had loads of gorgeous plaits in my mane. When I'd finished, I looked more like a loo brush than a smart show pony. Thankfully Cara had time to redo them!

Smudge

Whoops........!

Jump to it

When I moved to a new riding school I was determined to make a good impression. It was all going really well until one day the owner came to watch me in a jumping lesson. I was concentrating so hard on looking good I forgot I had a novice rider on my back. I took a huge leap over a small fence, clearing it by miles, but my rider went flying and landed in a pile of fresh poo – cringe! Luckily, the rider wasn't hurt and the yard owner thought it was hilarious!

Toby

Soooo criiiiinge!

Spooky sheep

I'd been really well behaved for ages and was feeling a bit mischievous. So, out on a hack I spooked every time I thought my rider, Hannah, wasn't paying enough attention. I thought it was really funny, until one of the invisible monsters turned out to be a very real, massive, scary sheep! I was so shocked I snorted and nearly fell over. Hannah thought it was really funny and told the whole yard about it when we got back.

Misty

What a mess

Some girls from the yard were poo-picking my paddock, so I went over to investigate. As I stretched my neck to sniff the barrow, one of them gave me a scratch on my fave itchy spot. I was so distracted I misjudged where the barrow was and knocked it over. The poo went everywhere and the girls were not impressed!

Pringle

Sleeping beauty

My owner, Orla, spent ages making sure I was gleaming as we had a show the next day. When she put me in my stable for the night, I forgot I was supposed to stay clean and accidentally slept in some poo. When I woke up I had a massive stain all down my neck. Orla was not very pleased with me when she saw it and had to bath me again – oops!

Bertie

Feeling cool

My rider, Bea, decided to take me cross-country schooling. It was a warm day, so when we got to the water complex I felt like cooling off and lay down in the water. Bea was so shocked all she could do was jump off and watch! Eventually I got up, but Bea wasn't very impressed that she had to spend the rest of the session sitting on a soggy saddle!

Crunchie

Kinda criiinge!

A WORK OF ART

Use our step-by-step guide to draw your fave pony

Get creative and have a go at drawing your fave pony! It's actually much easier than you think – just follow our simple steps. You can start by sketching his head, then have a go at his whole body, too.

PERFECT PORTRAIT

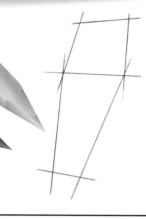 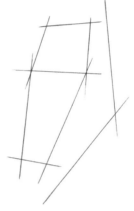 

Step 1
Draw three horizontal lines to mark the base of your pony's ears, eyes and nostrils. The distance from the top to the middle line will be half the distance between the middle and bottom lines. Now add four lines that outline the head. Remember that the ears should be closer together than the eyes, and the nostrils even closer.

Step 2
Add two angled lines on the right to mark out his cheek.

Step 3
Draw a circle for the nose, positioning it slightly to the right. The lower right-hand quarter of this circle will form your pony's chin. Next, create an oval shape that will become his cheek.

TOP TIP
Have a clear, close up photo of your fave pony's head to help you copy his features, such as his face markings.

Step 4
Now you have a rough outline, you can start sketching in the details. Try to make all your lines curve inwards or outwards, rather than drawing straight lines, so your pony's head looks more natural. Don't forget, too, that his ears should sit at the side of his head, not on top of it.

Step 5
Rub out any guide lines, then draw in the mane and forelock, and colour in your pony!

GET IN SHAPE

Step 1
Draw a square and add in two horizontal lines, a quarter and halfway up. In the top half draw an oval, plus two egg shapes that lean toward each other. From the highest point of the right-hand egg, draw a triangle for your pony's neck and a squared-off triangle for his head.

Step 2
Sketch a vertical guide line that drops down from just in front of your pony's withers and goes through his chest, and another slightly in from the edge of his hindquarters. Draw circles on these lines for the knee, hock and fetlock joints, making sure that the hock is higher than the knee. Then add his legs.

Adding an extra guide line from the hock to the hip can help you achieve the correct proportions for your pony's hindquarters.

Step 3
Add the second pair of legs, remembering that they're further away, so should be shorter. To ensure they're level, draw a line as a guide. Also add in more detail to your pony's head and body.

TOP TIP
To get a really light and smooth base colour, use the side of your pencil rather than the point.

Step 4
Draw the mane above the line of the neck, then add your pony's tail.

Step 5
To finish, outline your pony with a pen or pencil, then rub out your guide marks. Now colour him in!

TOP TIP
Shadowing gives a suggestion of depth. Add shadow under the chin, and behind the cheek, elbow and stifle, and under the legs furthest away.

EUROPEAN BREEDS

TRAKEHNER

The multi-talented Trakehner is regarded as the all-round competition horse

Fans of the Trakehner will tell you that this breed is the ultimate sport horse, who is equally at home doing dressage, showjumping or cross-country. They have a lighter build than most modern-day Warmblood horses, which makes them elegant and agile, yet they're strong and powerful, too.

FACT FILE

HEIGHT: 15.2hh-17hh

COLOUR: Any colour, but bay, black, grey and chestnut are most common

PLACE OF ORIGIN: Trakehnen in Prussia, a former German kingdom

KNOWN FOR: Their athleticism, stamina, trainability, good temperament, courage and flashy trot!

DID YOU KNOW?
Several of the Lloyds Bank black horses have been full or part-bred Trakehners, including Downlands Cancara in the 1980s and Holme Grove Prokofiev in 2012.

DID YOU KNOW?
Most modern day Trakehners can be traced back to two stallions, Perfectionist and Tempelhoiter.

History

The origins of the Trakehner can be traced all the way back to the 13th century, but the breed was developed in the early 18th century in Prussia, an historic former part of Northern Europe. The famous Trakehnen Stud was set up in 1732 by King Friedrich Wilhelm I who wanted to breed a modern cavalry horse that combined the good temperament and strength of heavier types, but was faster and lighter. He also wanted horses that were smart enough for his officers to ride, too.

DID YOU KNOW?
King Friedrich's Trakehnen Stud covered 15,000 acres.

Highs and lows

The versatile nature of the breed saw it grow in popularity, but these beautiful horses were dealt a cruel blow during World Wars I and II. As well as thousands being lost during the fighting, the famous stud was evacuated in 1944 when the Russian Army invaded East Prussia. Many of the horses were lost to the Russian troops. Other Trakehners belonging to local breeders and farmers were taken on a treacherous journey to safety, but from the thousands that set out only a few survived.

Luckily, the future of the breed was secured by incredible people who traced many of the missing horses and formed the Association of Breeders of the Warmblood Horse of Trakehner Origin (now called Trakehner Verband).

DID YOU KNOW?
Charlotte Dujardin scored a hat-trick of dressage wins at Windsor Horse Show in 2019 riding the Trakehner, Erlentanz.

Winner, winner

The breed's talent as a competition horse was recognised in the 1920s and 1930s, and Trakehners won six gold medals at the Berlin Olympic Games in 1936.

Since then, they've shone in all of the main equestrian disciplines and have featured on many of the German Equestrian Federation's dressage, showjumping and eventing teams.

They've also made their mark in driving and endurance riding, too!

Pure genius

Trakehner enthusiasts are super-proud of the breed, and breeding is closely monitored to ensure it stays true to type. Only the best stallions are accepted onto the stud book, and there's an annual grading that tests their gait, temperament and jumping ability.

With the Trakehner's talents given such high respect around the world, they've also been used to improve the bloodlines of several other breeds.

QUIZ
A NEW DIRECTION

Looking for something new to enjoy with your fave pony? Our fun quiz will help you choose the perfect sport to sign up for

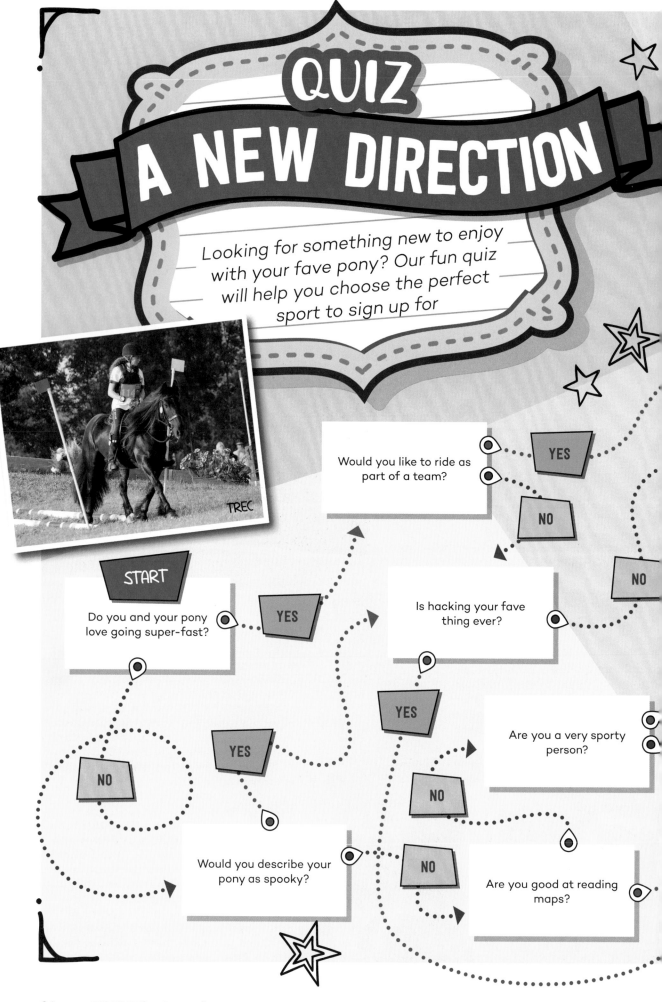

TREC

START

Do you and your pony love going super-fast?

YES

NO

Would you like to ride as part of a team?

YES

NO

Is hacking your fave thing ever?

NO

YES

Are you a very sporty person?

YES

NO

Would you describe your pony as spooky?

NO

Are you good at reading maps?

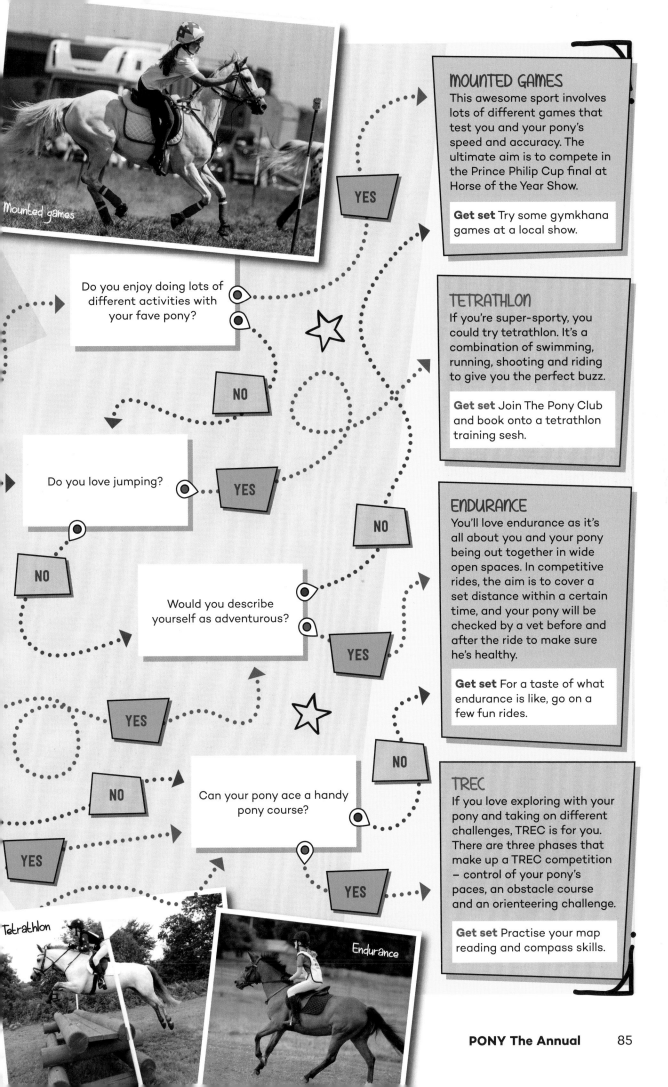

Mounted games

MOUNTED GAMES
This awesome sport involves lots of different games that test you and your pony's speed and accuracy. The ultimate aim is to compete in the Prince Philip Cup final at Horse of the Year Show.

Get set Try some gymkhana games at a local show.

YES

Do you enjoy doing lots of different activities with your fave pony?

NO

TETRATHLON
If you're super-sporty, you could try tetrathlon. It's a combination of swimming, running, shooting and riding to give you the perfect buzz.

Get set Join The Pony Club and book onto a tetrathlon training sesh.

Do you love jumping?

YES

NO

NO

Would you describe yourself as adventurous?

ENDURANCE
You'll love endurance as it's all about you and your pony being out together in wide open spaces. In competitive rides, the aim is to cover a set distance within a certain time, and your pony will be checked by a vet before and after the ride to make sure he's healthy.

Get set For a taste of what endurance is like, go on a few fun rides.

YES

YES

NO

NO

Can your pony ace a handy pony course?

TREC
If you love exploring with your pony and taking on different challenges, TREC is for you. There are three phases that make up a TREC competition – control of your pony's paces, an obstacle course and an orienteering challenge.

Get set Practise your map reading and compass skills.

YES

YES

Tetrathlon

Endurance

World Cup

JUMPING AND DRESSAGE FINALS

Everything you need to know about this exciting event

Save the date

The 2020 finals take place from 15-19 April in Las Vegas, USA.

GOTHENBURG 2019

Every year the world's best dressage riders and showjumpers head to the International Equestrian Federation (FEI) World Cup Finals. All the action takes place over five days as the riders compete to be crowned the champion!

DID YOU KNOW?
The FEI World Cup Jumping and Dressage Finals always takes place indoors.

Getting to the finals

The world is divided into four dressage and 16 showjumping leagues that hold qualifying rounds throughout the year. At each competition, riders accumulate points, with the top riders from the leagues qualifying to compete in the World Cup finals.

DID YOU KNOW?
The showjumping final celebrated its 40th anniversary in 2019.

DID YOU KNOW?
The jumps in each round are huge, with heights of 1.45–1.60m!

WORLD CUP SHOWJUMPING

With three days of top-level showjumping, there's plenty of action at this exciting event. Riders and horses compete in up to four rounds, over huge fences standing at 1.45-1.60m!

Only the top 20 combinations will get the chance to battle it out in the final round, where they'll try their best to go clear and claim the prestigious World Cup title.

WORLD CUP DRESSAGE

The first stage of the dressage finals is a Grand Prix test. All 18 riders must perform in front of seven judges, with the aim of qualifying for the Freestyle to Music. The winning combination in the music test claims the title!

Showjumping superstars

Nick Skelton and John Whitaker are the only two British riders to have won the FEI World Cup since the competition began in 1979. However, five riders have managed to claim the title three times, including 2019 winner, Steve Guerdat. Rodrigo Pessoa has enjoyed the most success at this competition, though, as he's the only rider to have held the title for three years on the trot (1998–2000) riding Baloubet du Rouet!

Dressage hall of fame

In its 33-year history only two riders have won the Dressage World Cup title three years in a row. In 2019, Isabell Werth and her horse Weihegold Old rode to victory, meaning they've been undefeated at the event since 2017.

Dutch rider Anky van Grunsven is a three-time winner, too, with Salinero. Anky also holds the record for the most wins, having claimed the title nine times!

Isabell Werth

Steve Guerdat

TIME TO SPARE

Ace your yard chores so you can enjoy more quality time with your fave pony

It's the perfect weather for a hack, but first you've got to feed your pony, muck out his stable, poo-pick his paddock and tidy up before the yard manager arrives. Phew – how are you going to get it all done in time? Just follow our top tips and you'll speed through those chores in no time at all...

TOP TIP
Even if you're trying to save time it's still really important that you do your yard jobs properly. So work smarter – don't cut corners!

1. PERFECT PREP

Prepare your pony's breakfast or morning haynet the night before, so you can grab it from the feed room or barn on your way to his stable. Making up feeds and haynets in advance is a clever way of saving time, and it's something you can do each weekend. Store the feeds in rodent-proof containers.

2. FOOD DELIVERY

If you know a friend's getting to the yard super-early, ask them if they can feed your pony for you. This means you'll be able to ride as soon as you get there. Your yard manager might be happy to do this for you, too, or set up a yard rota.

TOP TIP

Multi-tasking is a great way to get two jobs done at the same time. So, while your water bucket's filling up, fit in a quick task such as emptying the wheelbarrow.

3. OPEN SESAME

If you're going in and out of your pony's stable while he's inside, use a stable chain so you can leave the door open without your pony escaping. It means you don't have to waste time opening and shutting the door over and over again.

4. LITTLE AND OFTEN

You can make jobs like poo-picking so much easier and quicker by doing a little bit each day. Even just clearing up for five minutes at a time will save you facing a time-consuming mountain of muck at the weekend.

5. GO HALVES

Two pairs of hands will get pony chores done in half the time, so ask a friend on the yard if they want to team up with you. For example, one of you can top up the water buckets while the other fills haynets. Poo-picking can also be streamlined with two of you working together. Having someone to chat to will make chores more fun, too.

6. WHEELY CLEVER

Don't waste time walking backwards and forwards to the tack room with all your riding kit. Ask if you can tie your pony up next to the tack room to save you some steps, or load everything into a clean wheelbarrow and push it over to your pony's stable.

7. MAKE A CLEANER SWEEP

Tidying up won't be such an effort if you make less mess in the first place...
● carry loose hay in a sack or use small-holed nets which will shed fewer bits onto the yard
● brush off any hay that's clinging to your clothing before you leave your pony's stable or the hay barn
● don't overfill the wheelbarrow
● secure a sheet or net over your filled barrow on a windy day
● pick your pony's feet out before you bring him out of his stable

PONY MAG

MORE RIDING, MORE PONY CARE, MORE FUN!

Be a better rider with our fantastic training features and online videos

Learn everything you need to know about pony care

Meet BEN HOBDAY

Keep up to date with the latest rider gossip and behind-the-scenes horsey action

MAKE

a pony cushion

Sew this awesome cushion cover

TOP TIP
Visit
bit.ly/PONY_SEWING
for full instructions
on how to master
overstitch.

You'll need...

- ✓ a cushion cover that's 40x40cm
- ✓ tracing paper (or baking parchment)
- ✓ marker pen
- ✓ scissors
- ✓ sheets of felt
- ✓ pins
- ✓ needle and thread
- ✓ coloured ribbon

1. Print off or scale-up the cushion cover templates, then use tracing paper to copy them.

2. Use scissors to cut out the templates. You'll need one for the head, including the eyes and nostril, one for the mane, plus one for the forelock.

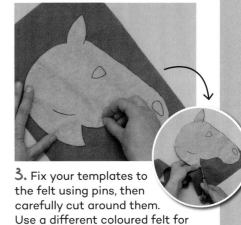

3. Fix your templates to the felt using pins, then carefully cut around them. Use a different coloured felt for your pony's head and mane.

TURN TO PAGE 101 FOR THE TEMPLATES

Ask an adult for help when using scissors and needles.

TOP TIP
If you don't want to sew, you could use fabric glue.

4. Layer the pieces of felt to form your pony's head, then fix them in place with pins. The more pins you use, the more secure it'll be.

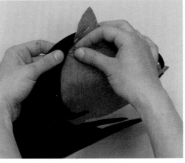

5. Use overstitch to attach the mane, forelock, eye and nostril to the head. Add a little sparkle to his eye by sewing a small white circle of felt inside it.

6. Lay the ribbon over the head to create the headcollar, then cut it to length. Leave a little extra to tuck underneath, so it doesn't fray. Then stitch or glue it in place.

7. Using overstitch again, sew the pony to the cushion cover. Make sure you only sew it to one side, though, or you won't be able to get a cushion inside!

8. Fill your cushion cover with an appropriate-sized cushion, then put it in pride of place on your bed or sofa.

WOW!

EUROPEAN BREEDS

LIPIZZANER

A staple of the famous Spanish Riding School, the Lipizzaner is a true dressage master!

DID YOU KNOW?
The very first guide to training Lipizzaners for the Spanish Riding School was written all the way back in 1898!

Not just a pretty face, these incredible horses are famed for their role in the Spanish Riding School in Vienna. There, they can be found performing extraordinary movements of classical dressage, and their training dates back hundreds of years.

History

The first Lipizzaner stud, Kladrub, is believed to have been founded in Austria in 1562 by Emperor Maximillian II. A similar stud was later formed in 1580 in Slovenia. This stud was named Lipizza, which is where the name Lipizzaner comes from.

At Lipizza, Barb, Arab and Spanish horses were combined to create the ideal horse for the military and riding schools for nobility.

In 1920 the Piber Federal Stud in Austria became the home for Vienna's Lipizzaners.

The breed thrived as it grew in popularity, but their numbers were threatened by the advancing Soviet army in 1945. Under the command of General George S Patton, the US Third Army rescued over 1,000 horses, including 375 Lipizzaners.

They were finally returned to the Spanish Riding School in 1955, and the 60th anniversary of Patton's rescue was celebrated in 2005.

FACT FILE

HEIGHT: 14.2hh to 16.1hh
COLOUR: Primarily white, though they can also be bay or black.
PLACE OF ORIGIN: Spain and Austria
KNOWN FOR: Their work in the Spanish Riding School, broad stature, compact build and long lifespan.

Wartime Lipizzaners

Between 1797 and 2007, Lipizzaners had to move home a lot due to war. Particularly in earlier years, these moves could well have saved them from extinction.

During World War II, most of Europe's Lipizzaners were moved to Czechoslovakia, along with all of Piber's breeding stock. As told in Disney's *Miracle of the White Stallions*, the US army rescued Lipizzaners towards the end of the war. Piber's horses were returned in 1952, and Lipizzaners finally came home to the Spanish Riding School in 1955.

DID YOU KNOW?
Originally, the Spanish Riding School taught cavalry riders how to prepare their horses for warfare.

DID YOU KNOW?
The Winter Riding School in Vienna was completed in 1729, and it's been home to the Spanish Riding School ever since!

The Spanish Riding School

Famous for their exciting performances in Vienna, it's here that the Lipizzaners learn how to do the awesome airs above ground. The first Spanish riding hall was built in 1572, making it the oldest arena in the world! Although it's located in Austria, Lipizzaners come from Spain, which is why it's known as the Spanish Riding School.

The Lipizzaners are put through their paces in several stages of training to become the amazing horses we know.

The stages are...
1. Forward riding
2. Campaign school
3. High-School dressage

These are pretty similar to the scales of training used in dressage today. Starting with putting a saddle on and all the way through to performing in Vienna, the training can take years – practice makes perfect!

AWESOME ADVENTURES

Some super-fun activities to add to your riding wish list

CANTER ALONG THE BEACH

Taking your fave pony for a blast along a sandy beach is one of the most exciting things you can do. Just find your nearest horse-friendly beach, check out the tide times and get some friends to meet you there. If you don't have your own pony you can book a ride with an equestrian centre that's close to the coast.

LEARN FROM A TOP RIDER

Loads of pro riders teach as well as compete, so why not book a lesson with your fave? Many celeb riders host clinics and demos, too, especially during the winter, so it's worth checking out local equestrian centres to see if they have any big names visiting soon.

RIDE AN ICELANDIC HORSE

The Icelandic Horse is unique because it has an extra-special gait called the tölt. It's a four-beat gait, so it's a bit like walking really fast, but it's super-smooth and comfortable and you'll feel like you're gliding along!

TAKE PART IN A FUN RIDE

These are organised rides that anyone can join in, and as the name suggests they're super-fun to do! They're a great way to explore beautiful countryside where hacking isn't usually allowed, and most fun rides will have a selection of jumps you can try, too!

DID YOU KNOW?
Icelandic Horses also have a flying pace, where the legs on each side move in pairs, and the horses are said to be able to reach 30mph – wow!

GO BAREBACK

As well as improving your bond with your fave pony, riding bareback is a brilliant way to improve your balance and seat. Try it first when your instructor's with you, and stay in an enclosed space. Start in walk and once you feel confident you could try trotting or have a go at canter.

DO A PAIRS HUNTER TRIAL

If you love going cross-country, why not make it double the fun by entering a pairs hunter trial class with a friend? You'll complete a course of fences together, and you can even jump some of them side-by-side!

HAVE A GO AT SIDE-SADDLE

Experience a totally different way of riding by having a go at side-saddle. You may find it feels a bit weird at first to ride with both legs on the same side of your pony, but you'll soon feel super-elegant – especially if you dress the part in a riding habit!

DID YOU KNOW?
Up until the 1940s it was correct for ladies to ride side-saddle rather than astride.

LEARN DRESSAGE MOVES ON A SCHOOLMASTER

Have you been inspired by Carl Hester and Charlotte Dujardin to perform fancy dressage moves, but you're not sure how? Lots of equestrian centres have experienced horses known as schoolmasters that you can book a lesson on. They know all the moves, so it's easier for an instructor to teach you how to apply the right aids to make them happen.

DISCOVER THE WORLD

It really is possible to explore the world on horseback, and you can go on a riding holiday to pretty much any country you fancy! Why not take a trip to the USA to round up cattle cowboy style, or head to Africa to ride super-close to zebra, giraffe, elephants and lions?

TAKE TO THE SKY

When the Pegasus horses go missing, it's up to Raya to rescue them

Raya had lived in Literia alongside the Pegasus flying horses her whole life. Her father, Arlo, was the Royal Horse Handler and looked after the Royal Pegasus herd for King Solace. She dreamed of one day following in her father's footsteps, so she spent all of her free time helping him.

The horses were so beautiful. To the untrained eye they all looked quite similar with white coats, a silvery mane and tail, and gold tinted feathers, but Raya could tell them apart easily. Some had a few dapples in their coats, while others had gold flecks, too. Every night, Raya would help her father settle them in the stables before heading to bed.

Disappearing into the night

A high-pitched neigh broke the quiet silence of the night, waking Raya with a jolt. She was immediately out of bed and racing down the stairs to check on the horses, but came to an abrupt halt when she noticed the yard gate swinging in the breeze. She couldn't process what she was seeing. The gate was locked every night to keep the Pegasus herd safe and secure.

"Raya, what are you doing out here?" Arlo asked as he barrelled past her. "Go back inside where it's safe."

"But, the horses..." Raya stuttered in response. "I said go inside!" her father snapped, barely glancing at her as he made his way to the yard. Raya ignored him, following him into the stable block. The yard was deserted except for a few golden feathers left by the 30 winged horses. Tears filled Raya's eyes as she looked around at the empty space. Where had they gone? Another piercing neigh rang out. Raya span round, searching for the source of the noise. In the very back of the barn, she saw a flash of movement and she raced forward, only stopping when she reached the furthest stable.

There in the back of the box was Orion, the youngest of the herd, struggling in a thick, glowing net. "Shhh, boy," Raya said soothingly as she approached, looking him over for obvious injuries. "Dad! Orion's still here, but he's stuck," she called over her shoulder. He was beside her in a flash. Orion was so tangled in the net that they had to cut him free. Once the last strand was snipped from his body, Orion struggled to his feet, his eyes wild and his body shaking in terror.

"We need to find out what happened." Arlo spoke softly, while Raya stood in front of Orion, resting her forehead against his

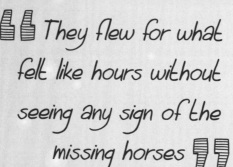

neck and gently stroking his silky coat. Immediately, images flashed through her mind.

Raya spoke urgently. "Men, dressed in black, came. They took everyone, I don't know where." The images stopped, just as abruptly as they had started and Raya staggered back, clutching her head, reeling from what she had seen. "These horses can do many amazing things," her dad said, smiling kindly at her. "I must go to the King for help," he added, running his hand through his hair. "Go and wake your mother. Tell her what's happened and that I'll be back as soon as I can." Raya didn't have time to respond as she watched her father leave. He strode swiftly down the yard and disappeared into the night.

Time to act

Raya knew it would take at least a day for her father to return from the King, as the palace was half a day's ride from here. They needed to look for the herd now. "We must find them, Ori," she said desperately as she stroked his silvery mane. "I could take you," a strong voice ribboned through her mind. "We can follow their scent." She glanced at Orion, not at all surprised by hearing his voice after what he'd shown her earlier. "Are you sure?" she asked, while he nodded his head vigorously. Orion positioned himself next to an old tree stump for Raya to mount. She climbed on his back, settling herself in front of his wings. "Hold on!" was the only warning Orion gave her before he took off at a gallop. Once Raya was convinced he couldn't go any faster, he opened his powerful, golden wings and they soared into the air.

"Wow!" she breathed in awe. "I can see for miles!"

"Keep an eye out for my herd," Orion instructed her. "Their scent is still strong. They've been taken east, toward the border." Raya scanned the dark land ahead of her, making use of the light from the full moon.

They flew for what felt like hours without seeing any sign of the missing horses. As the sky lightened, with the sun beginning to peek over the horizon, Raya felt helpless and very tired. She leant forward to tell Orion that they should stop to rest, when a glimmer of gold caught her eye.

"What's that? she pointed. "I'm not sure," he answered. "Hang on, I'll fly closer..." Orion turned, slowing the beat of his wings to allow them to descend.

"I think it's them! Ori, look!" Raya whispered, nearly slipping off his back in her excitement. "You're right –

> *They flew for what felt like hours without seeing any sign of the missing horses*

it looks like a wing. I'll land and we can get closer on hoof." Raya shut her eyes as Ori landed swiftly. She slipped from his back and together they edged closer to the thieves' hideout.

Daring rescue

Peering through the trees, Raya counted four men guarding the missing herd. A large canvas sheet had been stretched between four trees to camouflage the horses from above, and each had a piece of glowing rope around their neck. Thankfully, Pyxis, the herd's stallion, had stretched out one wing beyond the makeshift cover so it shined in the light, which Raya had spotted from above.

"This had better be worth all the hassle," one of the men grunted. "It'll take us days to reach the border travelling like this."

"Stop complaining, Gregor," the largest of the four men replied. "These beasts have magical powers. They hold the key to ruling Literia. This herd is the source of King Solace's magic and without them he's totally at our mercy. Soon, we'll be in control of Literia! We can't move them during the day or we'll easily be spotted."

"Here's the plan," Raya hissed as quietly as she could. "Ori, can you try and distract them? Make it seem like you've escaped and I'll get the others out." Orion nodded once, before turning and gliding silently through the trees. Once he was out of sight, Raya crept as far forward as she dared and waited.

"Hey! One of them's loose," came a shout. The men all sprang to their feet. "Gregor, get the charmed net. We need to catch him now!" The largest man immediately took charge, directing the other thieves where to go. Crossing her fingers that Orion wouldn't get caught, Raya dashed towards the horses.

Mission accomplished

"Come! Quickly!" Raya beckoned the horses to follow her, but they didn't move. "Please, before they get back," she begged desperately, but the herd ignored her pleas. Then Pyxis stepped forward very slowly, as though he was walking through treacle. Raya pressed her hand urgently against his neck so she could hear him speak.

"It's the rope," his deep voice rumbled in her mind. "It helps them control us. You must remove it." She nodded, immediately taking the rope from around Pyxis' neck. Working as quickly as she could, Raya freed the horses from their magical bonds and urged them away. Just as she removed the last rope she heard the men returning.

"Let's go, now!" She led the herd into the cover of the trees without looking back, travelling deeper into the wood. She heard clearly the bellows of rage and surprise as the men discovered the Pegasus horses were missing. She knew time was short, and they had to go, but she couldn't leave without Orion. Suddenly, he appeared at her side, trotting along next to her. "There's a clearing up ahead we can take off from," he told her as he stooped down. "Get on my back. We've got to hurry, the thieves are on our tracks."

When Raya and Orion reached the clearing the horses were already taking to the skies. Soon it was just Orion and Raya left. She felt a surge of power as the winged horse rushed forward and took off, seconds before the four men burst into the clearing.

Home again

Raya couldn't believe she'd managed to rescue the horses by herself. The journey home was quite uneventful and Raya was eager to see her father and tell him the good news. All the horses landed safely and she was seeing them back into the barn when her father returned with King Solace.

"Raya! What's going on?" her father demanded, somewhat confused to see the Pegasus horses back in their stables. "Orion and I went after the thieves," she explained in a rush. "They were planning to take over Literia by stealing the horses and controlling their magic. Orion cleverly distracted them and I got the horses free..." She trailed off under Arlo's stern gaze. "That's quite a tale," King Solace chuckled, looking astonished. "You can explain it all a little later, but thank you for rescuing the horses. Rest assured my army will catch those responsible. The whole kingdom and I owe you a great debt." With a grateful smile he turned away before issuing orders to his army.

Raya received a medal of honour for her bravery. She still helps her dad look after the Pegasus herd, but thankfully no further attempts have been made to steal them. In some ways it's been a bit boring in Literia. But with a whole herd of flying horses around it's never too dull, and despite her dad's half-hearted protests, she and Orion sneak away to go flying together whenever they can.

THE ANSWERS

Page 20 — GUESS WHO?

1 C, **2** C, **3** B, **4** B, **5** C, **6** C, **7** A, **8** C, **9** B, **10** A, **11** B, **12** B

Page 46 — LET'S GO HACKING

1 A, **2** B, **3** A, **4** C, **5** B, **6** C, **7** C, **8** A, **9** B

Page 58 — UNIQUE UNICORNS

Mostly As: Fire Unicorn
Your pony's got a huge personality and loves to go fast! He can be a bit impatient, but it's only because he wants to get the job done. He's also very loyal and loves you loads.

Mostly Bs: Earth Unicorn
He's known for being super-sensible and is usually a calming influence on his pony pals. You can always depend on him and he's the pony that everyone wants to ride!

Mostly Cs: Air Unicorn
Air unicorns are very clever and logical. Riding your pony has taught you loads, as he doesn't let you get away with anything and you always have to concentrate.

Mostly Ds: Water Unicorn
Water unicorns can lack confidence, which means your pony may need a little reassurance from you. You have an amazing bond with him and know he'd do absolutely anything for you.

Page 70 — STAR TREATMENT

Mostly carrots
Congrats, you did an amazing job helping Emily look after Star. You're a pony-care pro and know how to keep a pony happy and healthy.

Mostly buckets
Emily was really grateful for your help with Star, but it's a good idea to brush up on your pony-care skills for next time. You can keep improving by reading all the fab articles in PONY mag!

Mostly hoofpicks
Oh dear, you weren't super-confident about caring for Star. But don't worry – why not offer to help other friends out with their ponies? Then, if anyone else goes away, you'll know exactly what to do. It'll be great experience for when you get your own pony, too!

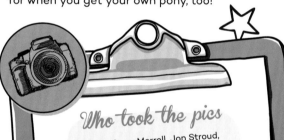

Who took the pics

Photography Lucy Merrell, Jon Stroud, Bob Atkins, shutterstock.com
Cover photo Lucy Merrell
p16-17 catwalker/shutterstock.com, Olympia/ Kit Houghton, Hickstead/Nigel Goddard
p20-21 Mark Todd Collection, Katie Neat Photography, Kit Houghton/Mitsubishi Motors Badminton Horse Trials
p22-23 FEI/Jon Stroud
p64-65 Horse of the Year Show/Kevin Wright, Karen Piercy
p80-81 Illustrations by Helena Öhmark and Rebecca Öhmark
p83 Windsor Horse Show
p84-85 TREC GB, Sammie Palmer
p86-87 FEI/Liz Gregg/Charlie Crowhurst/ Getty Images
p94-95 Spanish Riding School/René van Bakel/Michael Rzepa
p96 John Aron
p102-103 Illustrations by Helena Öhmark and Rebecca Öhmark

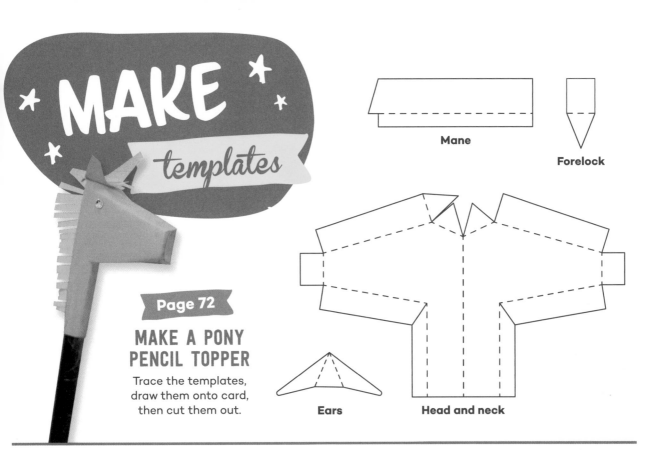

MAKE templates

Mane

Forelock

Page 72

MAKE A PONY PENCIL TOPPER

Trace the templates, draw them onto card, then cut them out.

Ears

Head and neck

Page 92

MAKE A PONY CUSHION

Draw the grid to size on two A4 pieces of paper and copy the shape.

7cm

7cm

To download the template in full size, head to bit.ly/PNY_ANNUAL_CUSHION

THE MISADVENTURES OF CHARLIE!

I bet I could be a vlogger, it can't be that difficult.

This Esme   62,864 views

What are you doing, Charlie?

Looking for my video camera...

Got it!

Oooh, what are you filming?

LATER THAT DAY

Aaaand my first video is live!

This is so exciting.

Charlie! Have you seen how many likes your video has?

No? Show me!

They love me!

Let's make another video.

Thanks for your support, everyone! I'll be posting one video a week, so stay tuned!

So, where are we filming?

I reckon the lake would look cool.

Erm, I'm doing all the work here, Charlie.

Coming...

This video is all about how I became famous.

PONY

I'm going to change, don't do anything until I'm back.

That'll teach him not to do any work!

UPLOADING 99%